Golden Rule Series

(The Modern McGuffey Readers)

Open Windows
Open Doors
Open Roads
Paths to Follow
Frontiers to Explore
Widening Horizons

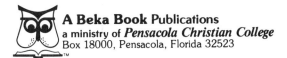 **A Beka Book** Publications
a ministry of *Pensacola Christian College*
Box 18000, Pensacola, Florida 32523

Paths

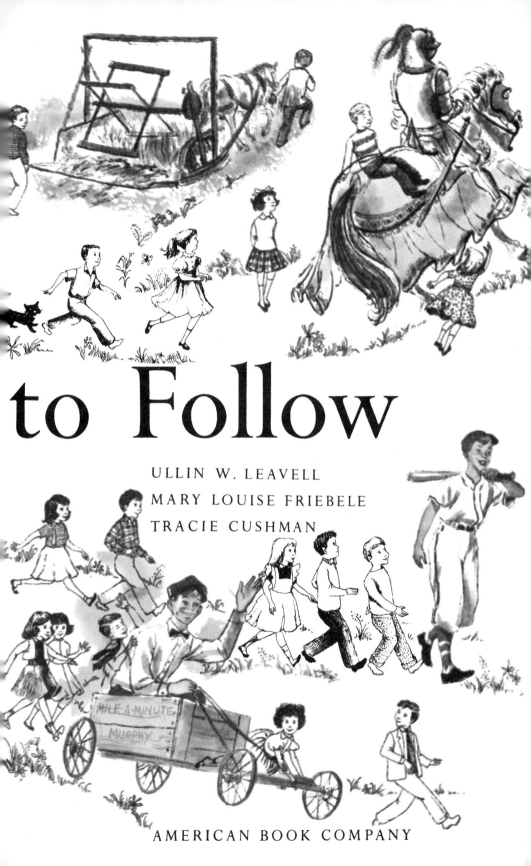

to Follow

ULLIN W. LEAVELL

MARY LOUISE FRIEBELE

TRACIE CUSHMAN

AMERICAN BOOK COMPANY

Paths to Follow

REVISED EDITION

Golden Rule Series

(The Modern McGuffey Readers)

ULLIN W. LEAVELL
*Formerly Professor of Education
and Director of
McGuffey Reading Clinic
University of Virginia
Charlottesville, Virginia*

MARY LOUISE FRIEBELE
*Professional Writer
for Children
Clearwater, Florida*

TRACIE CUSHMAN
*Formerly Classroom Teacher
Grand Rapids Public Schools
Grand Rapids, Michigan*

Sponsored by The Palmer Foundation, Texarkana, Arkansas-Texas

——————————————— 1982 PRINTING ———————————————

Acknowledgments

For permission to use and adapt copyrighted material, grateful acknowledgment is made to the following:

American Book Company for "What the Minutes Say" and "The Seven Sticks" from *McGuffey's Third Eclectic Reader*, copyright, 1896, by American Book Company; and for "Why the Sea Is Salt" by Mary Howitt from *McGuffey's Fourth Eclectic Reader*, copyright, 1896, by American Book Company.

Association for Childhood Education International and Mrs. John Gould Fletcher for "The Magic Button" from "Buttons," copyright by Charlie May Simon, from *Told Under Spacious Skies*, copyright, 1952, published by The Macmillan Company.

Association for Childhood Education International and Mrs. Mildred Geiger Gilbertson for "House of the Singing Windows" from *Told Under the Stars and Stripes*, copyright, 1945, published by The Macmillan Company.

The Bobbs-Merrill Company, Inc., for "Knights of the Silver Shield" from *Why the Chimes Rang and Other Stories* by Raymond Macdonald Alden, copyright, 1906, 1934. By special permission of the publishers, The Bobbs-Merrill Company, Inc.

Thomas Y. Crowell Company, New York, for "Brother Francis" from *God's Troubadour* by Sophie Jewett, copyright, 1938, by Edith Jewett; and for "All Things Bright and Beautiful" by C. Frances Alexander from *A Treasury of Verse for Little Children*.

E. P. Dutton & Co., Inc., for "Giving Is Thanks" by Amy Morris Lillie from *Book of Three Festivals*, published by E. P. Dutton & Co., Inc., copyright, 1946, by Gateway, reprinted and adapted by permission; and for quotation from "Of Courtesy" from *A Poet's Proverbs* by Arthur Guiterman, copyright, 1924, by E. P. Dutton & Co., Inc. Renewal, 1952, by Mrs. Arthur Guiterman.

Mrs. Ziva D. Giloane for "Two Brothers from Mount Moriah" from *Jack and Jill*, copyright, 1953, by Ziva D. Giloane.

Houghton Mifflin Company for "The Golden Touch" from *A Wonderbook and Tanglewood Tales*, 1889 Edition, by Nathaniel Hawthorne; and for quotation from "A Psalm of Life" from *Complete Poetical Works of Henry Wadsworth Longfellow*, 1893 Edition, by Henry Wadsworth Longfellow.

The Instructor and Josephine Robertson for "The Best Kiter," copyright, 1952, reprinted by permission of publisher and author.

Lantern Press, Inc., for "The Good Sport" by Charles Coombs, reprinted from *Young Readers Sports Stories*, copyright, 1950, by A. L. Furman, Lantern Press, Inc.

Mother's Magazine, David C. Cook Publishing Co., Elgin, Illinois, and Mae Hurley Ashworth for "A Rhyme to Read" by Mae Hurley Ashworth, copyright, 1946.

Story Parade, Inc., for "Valentines for America" by Mildred Lawrence, copyright, 1953, by *Story Parade, Inc.*, reprinted and adapted by permission; and for "Dog to Be Proud Of" by Maude Beery, copyright, 1948, by *Story Parade, Inc.*, reprinted and adapted by permission; and for "Riding the Pony Express" by Marion Garthwaite, copyright, 1949, by *Story Parade, Inc.*, reprinted and adapted by permission.

Wee Wisdom for "Pennies for Joy" by Mae Hurley Ashworth, copyright, 1942.

Mrs. Laura Ingalls Wilder, Mrs. Rose Wilder Lane, and George T. Bye for "Indians in the House" from *Little House on the Prairie* by Laura Ingalls Wilder, copyright, 1935, published by Harper & Brothers.

The artists who drew the pictures in this book are as follows:

Cover by Lucile Newman and Irene Haas

Lee Ames, pp. 26–31, 244–251
Sheilah Beckett, pp. 48–49, 98–99, 204–205, 221–227, 242–243
James Caraway, pp. 196–201
Hertha Depper, pp. 63–67
Irv Docktor, pp. 262–267
Seymour Fleishman, pp. 70–75, 216–219, 232
Bob Frankenberg, pp. 35–38, 150–156, 176–180
Irene Haas, pp. 2, 3

Robert Henneberger, pp. 138–143, 234–239
Ursula Koering, pp. 89–95, 254–259
Joe and Beth Krush, pp. 54–60, 122–127, 168–173, 194
Oscar Liebman, pp. 183–189, 205–213
Jean Michener, pp. 34, 52, 102–104, 148
Lucile Newman, pp. 40–45, 130–135
Sari, pp. 51, 100, 106–111
Kate Seredy, pp. 18–23, 86–87, 159–165
Tracy Sugarman, pp. 10–15, 78–83, 114–119, 270–277

Stories in This Book

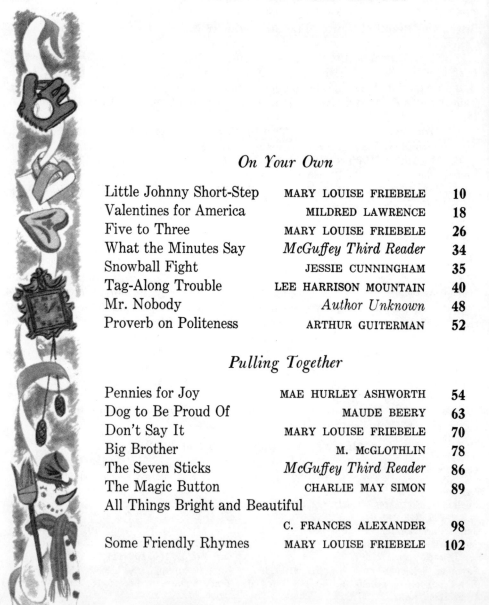

Winners All

Stories of Great People

Stories That Your Grandfather Liked

Stories of Other Days

On Your Own

Tools for Enjoyment

Have you discovered the fun of doing things well and knowing *how* you do them? This book will help you find that kind of fun in reading and in using words.

Which of the things named below do you think are really important for someone who wants to read well and speak well?

1. To know how to count the letters in a word
2. To know how to understand and master unknown words
3. To know what book had a certain big word in it
4. To know how to say words so that other people will understand them

Of course, number 2 and number 4 are the important things.

Now look carefully at these words: *big, bag, beg, bug*. They look quite a lot alike, but each one sounds different from the others when you say it. Can you tell why? What makes *big, bib,* and *bit* sound different? *Rag, bag,* and *tag?*

One letter does it in each case. One letter with a different sound makes the whole word sound different.

When you know that *letters stand for sounds*, you know something you can use as a tool to help you read well. The more you know about words, the more reading tools you will have. That is why there are activities for every story in this book, and a wordbook at the end. They will help give you the tools you need to get more enjoyment from your reading.

Little Johnny Short-Step

Johnny limped as fast as he could, but still he could not keep up. As the other boys left him behind, Johnny hated them, he hated school, he hated the whole world.

But in the reading room, he forgot about his limp. A new baseball book was on the table, and Johnny picked it up eagerly.

As Johnny sat turning the pages, staring at the pictures of the players, the walls of the room seemed to stretch away. In his daydream, he saw himself at the ball park with the crowd cheering and shouting for him. "Come on, Johnny, hit it, boy!"

The bases were loaded as Johnny stood ready to swing.

The ball came at him and then — crack! Up, up, and out it sailed. Johnny started to run. His flying feet touched first base, raced on to second base, then on past third.

He heard a roar from the crowd. The ball had bounced away from the fielder. Johnny raced on and slid home — safe!

Johnny rubbed his eyes. The walls of the room closed back around him. He knew that he could dream all day, but he would never bat the baseball and then run faster and faster while the crowd cheered.

He could read all of the baseball books in the world, but he would never slide into home plate. He could know all about the game, but he could never, never be on a baseball team.

When a shadow fell across Johnny, he covered the book with his arms. He knew that the boys in his class always laughed at him when he talked to them about baseball.

They could not understand why a boy with a short leg liked to read about a game that he could never play. So they would laugh at him and call him Little Johnny Short-Step.

"Say, that looks like a new baseball book. May I see it?" Bob Green, the captain of the high-school baseball team, was leaning over Johnny's shoulder. Bob gave Johnny a friendly push. "Move over," he said.

Bob flipped the pages of the book. "What are you doing with a book on baseball?" he asked. "Do you like baseball?"

"Yes," Johnny answered in a low voice. He was beginning to ache and to curl up deep inside, the way he always did when someone laughed at him.

Johnny wished he could crawl away into a hard, tight shell, like a turtle, and hide. He pushed his hands deep into his pockets while he waited. Now Bob would laugh and call him Little Johnny Short-Step.

But Bob only put his hand on Johnny's shoulder. "Oh, sure," he said. "I remember now. My little brother is in your class. You're Johnny — you're the boy who knows all about baseball."

He turned another page or two of the book without looking at Johnny.

"Since you like baseball so much," Bob said then, "why don't you come out and watch us practice some afternoon?"

Johnny tried to say "thank you," but he couldn't make the words come out of his tight throat. He could only nod his head.

"Good," Bob said. "I'll see you." And he walked away.

Slowly Johnny uncurled his fingers and took his hands out of his pockets. Then he sat quietly while the tight ache eased into a wonderful feeling of surprise and happiness.

He had never dared to go before because he was afraid the boys would laugh at him. But now the captain of the team had asked him, Little Johnny Short-Step, to come and watch the team practice!

That afternoon, as soon as school was over, Johnny limped happily out to the baseball field. He pulled himself up on a low fence at one side of the field.

Johnny's eyes were shining as he sat and listened to the crack of the bat against the ball and the shouts of the boys.

When Bob trotted out on the field, he noticed Johnny sitting on the fence and waved to him. Johnny was so proud and happy he thought his heart would pound right out of his body.

By the fourth afternoon, he knew the names of all the boys who came out to practice. He knew how they pitched, and how they batted, and how they ran.

As soon as he climbed up on the fence, he forgot his limp. He forgot the boys who had laughed at him. He even forgot to be quiet so no one would notice him. He forgot everything but the game.

"Feet first!" he shouted at one of the new boys on the team. "Slide feet first!"

Johnny had forgotten that he was sitting on a fence. He bounced up and down as he yelled, and slid right off the fence to the ground.

Bob happened to see him fall. He ran to him quickly, but Johnny had already pulled himself up by holding onto the fence. "Hello, Johnny," Bob said. "That's not a very good place to sit. Come and sit on the bench with us."

Johnny limped proudly by Bob's side and sat down on the bench. The other boys smiled at him.

Johnny tried to remember to be quiet, but the game was just too exciting. "You're playing in too close!" he yelled at Bob in center field.

Bob moved back just in time to catch a fly ball.

The boys on the bench all looked surprised. "You really *do* know baseball, don't you!" one of them said to Johnny.

When Bob came back to the bench, he grinned and said to Johnny, "Stick around. You'll make a player of me yet!"

After that, Johnny sat on the players' bench every day.

The boys talked to Johnny about baseball, and they listened to him when he talked. They soon found out that he knew some things about the game that they didn't know. And if they were uncertain about a play, they often asked Johnny.

One day Bob said to him, "You can't sit here on the bench and be lazy all your life. We need a bat boy, and we'd like for you to give it a try. All right?"

"All right," Johnny said quickly. He ducked down and picked up one of the bats. He couldn't let anyone, not even Bob, see how happy he was.

He quickly learned which bat each player liked best, and he had it ready for him. Whenever a batter dropped his bat as he started to run, Johnny picked it up almost before it hit the ground.

The boys practiced harder and harder as the time for their first big game drew near. Everyone on the team wanted to win, but Johnny wanted his team to win more than anything in the world.

At last there were only two days left before the first game. When Johnny limped out to the field, he saw Bob and another boy talking together.

Once Johnny would have felt a tight ache begin inside. He would have curled his fingers in his pockets. But now these were his friends. He grinned at them, and they smiled back.

After practice was over, Johnny picked up the last bat.

"Johnny," Bob called to him, "come here a minute."

Johnny looked up. The whole team was standing there, smiling at him.

Johnny limped over to them. Why were they all looking so pleased? They still had that big game to win, didn't they?

"Johnny," said Bob, "the fellows and I think you should have a uniform like ours to wear for the baseball games. Here it is." One of the other boys pulled a big box from behind him and handed it to Johnny.

Johnny hung onto the box with both hands. He was too happy to speak. He was the happiest boy in all the world. Little Johnny Short-Step had made the team, and this time he wasn't dreaming!

A Big Change

At the beginning of this story, Johnny hated himself and everybody else. But by the end of the story, he was as happy as he could be. What was one cause for this change? Write 1, 2, or 3.

1. Johnny no longer limped.
2. Johnny had made friends.
3. Johnny had stopped reading about baseball.

Reading for Ideas

Reading is much more fun if you do not have to ask the teacher for help whenever you meet a new word. Often you can discover what a new word says by reading all the other words in the sentence. Knowing the idea of the sentence will help you read the new word.

If you get the idea of each of these sentences, you will know what word should appear in each blank. Write those words on your paper.

1. Since one of his legs was shorter than the other, Johnny walked with a __.
2. Sometimes when Johnny tried to speak, he felt a tight, aching feeling in his —, and the words would not come out.
3. Bob made his longest hits when the — threw him a fast ball.
4. When Johnny watched the team practice, he sat on the wooden __ with the players.
5. When Bob and the other boys gave Johnny a uniform, he really felt that he belonged on their baseball __.

16

From Short-Step to Shortstop

Look carefully at the two words *step* and *stop*. Only one letter is different in these words: *e* appears in *step* where *o* appears in *stop*. However, the words sound different and have different meanings.

The letters in a word stand for sounds. When you change even one letter in a word, you are likely to change the sound and meaning of that word.

Change the *c* in *care* to *d*, and you have *dare*.

Change the *a* in *draw* to *e*, and you have *drew*.

Write the following words on a piece of paper. Underline the letter you should change in each word to make the name of the picture beside it.

bat

class

slid

feed

yell

rang

Valentines for America

Anya almost ran as she hurried down the country road. She could hardly wait to get home so she could tell Mama about the valentines.

When she reached the gate, she stood, for a moment, looking at the house where she and Mama and Papa now lived.

To anyone else, her house might look like just another old weather-beaten farmhouse. But to Anya, it was the most wonderful house in the world.

Everything about America was wonderful, thought Anya, even if the children at school sometimes laughed at her.

But after tomorrow they would not make fun of her any more. Starting tomorrow with the valentines, she was going to do everything the American way.

"Mama!" Anya called out, opening the door. "Could Papa maybe take me to town now in the truck to buy valentines?"

Mama did not answer. She must have gone into town with Papa today. She often did that, when she got lonesome out here all by herself.

"Mama is different, too," Anya said to herself. "And she doesn't speak American so well yet, either."

Then her thoughts jumped back to the valentines.

The gay Valentine Box that Miss Riggs had brought with her to school that morning had been a big surprise to Anya. She had learned that tomorrow, for Valentine's Day, everyone would bring valentines to drop in the red and white box.

After school, Anya stood by Miss Riggs, waiting quietly until she was told she could speak. "Where do you buy the valentines, please?" she asked.

"At the ten-cent store," Miss Riggs had said. "Or you can make pretty ones yourself out of red and white paper. They're fun to make."

"Yes, Miss Riggs. Thank you, please."

The children had laughed then, and Anya had turned red. It was hard to remember not to say "please" and "thank you" at the same time.

"But even though they did laugh at me," she had said to herself, "I found out where to buy the valentines. And that was the important thing."

On the way home, she had told her friend George, the bus driver, all about it. "Should I buy one for everybody in the class?" she had asked.

"If you want to," George had said. "But you can do as you please, Anya. This is a free country, you know."

"Better I do buy for all," Anya decided then. "Even the ones who laugh. They teach me when I make a mistake, so I won't say it wrong again."

Now, sitting in the empty kitchen, Anya was afraid that everything might turn out wrong tomorrow. If she had nothing to put in the box, the boys and girls would think she did not like the American ways.

"I could maybe walk to town," she thought. But a quick look at the clock told her that she could not. It was six miles to town, and the stores would be closed long before she could get there.

"Or I could try to make some valentines the way Miss Riggs said," Anya went on thinking. But she knew she had no red and white paper.

In fact, she had no paper at all, except the yellow kind with lines across it that they used at school. And that kind would be wrong, she thought.

Anya poured herself a big glass of milk and spread some of Mama's good butter on a thick piece of homemade bread. Then she sat down and tried to think about what she could do. Mama always said a little food made everything look brighter.

Anya could remember how it had felt to be hungry all the time in her own country after the war. But here in America things were different, of course. People could eat as much as they wanted whenever they wanted.

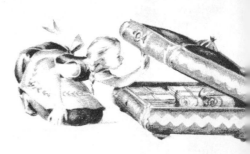

The first things Mama had bought for their new house were pans for baking cakes and cookies. "Plain eating is nice — wonderful, even," Mama had said. "But pretty tastes just three times as good."

And so Mama's cookies and cakes were always iced with pretty flowers and leaves, and on Christmas, with a beautiful Christmas tree.

"Christmas!" thought Anya suddenly. "Maybe some of the plain red wrapping paper from Christmas would do for those valentines! I could maybe find a piece left somewhere."

So Anya hunted in every drawer and cupboard in the whole house. But it was no use. Mama was too neat. She had thrown all the Christmas wrappings away.

"There must be some way," Anya told the fat black and white cat that came rubbing around her legs. "Papa says there is almost always a way if only you think hard enough. Maybe Papa will help me think of something."

Anya had supper all ready when Mama and Papa came in. Mama sniffed happily. "Smells good," she said.

"Mama thinks that the very best thing about America is the food," Papa said laughing.

"Second best, maybe," said Mama cheerfully. "First best is doing what you please."

"That's what George said!" cried Anya. Then she added, "Papa, I've been thinking and thinking. I have an American thing to do before tomorrow and nothing to do it with."

"Nothing?" replied Papa, smiling. "Think harder, maybe. Nobody ever had *nothing!*"

So Anya thought harder. Her thoughts wandered all over the house, upstairs and down, and found nothing she could use to make valentine cards.

Anya's thoughts wandered back into the kitchen as she watched Mama cut the cake she had baked that morning. It had beautiful red flowers on it, and Anya said, "It's too pretty to eat almost."

Then suddenly she cried, "Papa! I thought harder!"

Next morning, Anya got on the bus carrying a large brown package. "What's in it?" everyone asked.

"My valentines," said Anya proudly.

"Must be big ones, then," somebody said. "They might not go in the Valentine Box."

Anya said nothing. She had thought hard, the way Papa had said. And even if her valentines were not like the American ones, they were the best she could do.

Anyway, George had said, "Do as you please. It's a free country." Now was as good a time as any to find out if this was really true.

When Anya handed her big package over to Miss Riggs, the teacher said, "Are these your valentines, Anya? Put them in the box, please."

"They won't go in the box," said Anya. She felt her face getting red again. "Will you open them for me?"

Miss Riggs smiled at her and said, "Why, yes, of course," and everyone crowded around to watch her open the package.

There, covered with bright red icing, was a large, heart-shaped cooky for every girl and boy in the class!

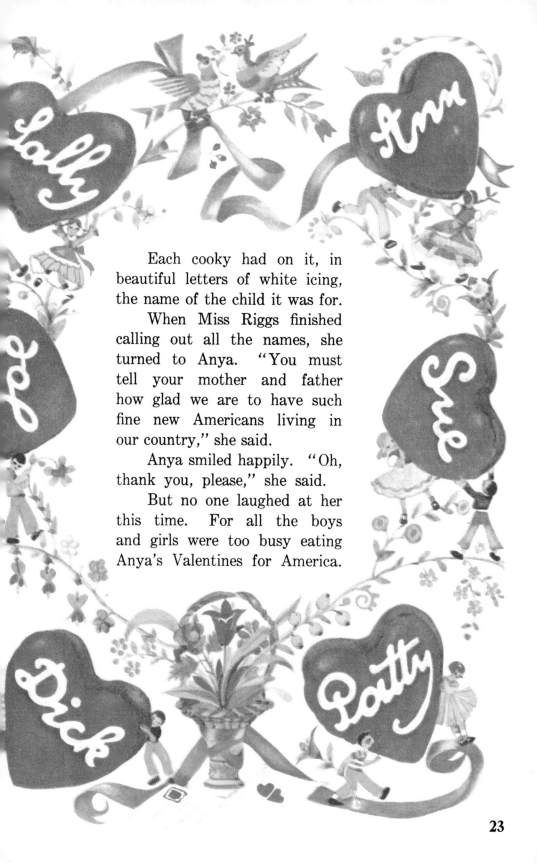

Each cooky had on it, in beautiful letters of white icing, the name of the child it was for.

When Miss Riggs finished calling out all the names, she turned to Anya. "You must tell your mother and father how glad we are to have such fine new Americans living in our country," she said.

Anya smiled happily. "Oh, thank you, please," she said.

But no one laughed at her this time. For all the boys and girls were too busy eating Anya's Valentines for America.

Getting the Point

Every good story has a point. The point of the story is the idea that the writer wants the reader to remember. Which of these two points was the writer of *Valentines for America* more interested in having you remember? Write 1 or 2.

1. Making cookies for valentines is a good idea.
2. Making the best use of whatever you have is a good idea.

Writing the Right Word

Some pairs of words sound alike but are spelled differently and have different meanings. A number of these pairs appear in the following sentences. On your paper write the word from each pair that carries out the meaning of the sentence.

Anya wanted to make the (right, write) kind of valentines, but she (knew, new) she didn't have time to (by, buy) colored paper. It would take (hours, ours) to walk all the way to town and back. She did not (know, no) what to do.

"I'll (bee, be) the only one at school who didn't bring valentines," Anya said to herself. After she (ate, eight) dinner, a wonderful idea came to her. She baked some big, heart-shaped cookies.

The next morning Anya (wrapped, rapped) up the cookies and took them (to, too) school. The other children at school liked (there, their) cooky valentines much better than (there, their) paper valentines.

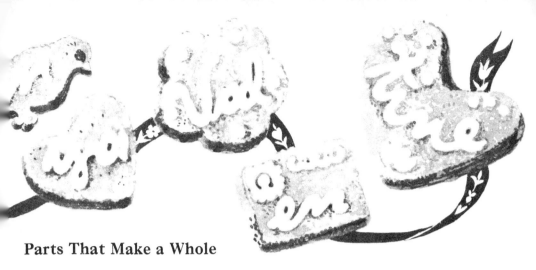

Parts That Make a Whole

Perhaps you had never met the word *Anya* until you read *Valentines for America*. But you could read the word, couldn't you? You could read a strange word like *Anya* because you saw that the first part is like the word *an*. The second part is like the *y* in *you* and the *a* in *idea*. You could read *Anya* because it is made up of sounds of words that you already know.

Of course, you need to know how to find the right parts of words. If you look at the word *Anya* and say *An-ya*, fine! But if you look at the word *Anya* and say *Any-a*, you are in trouble. Parts of words are called syllables. A syllable is one or more letters said all at once, like the *An* in *Anya*.

Write these words from the story in three lists. In your first list, write the six words that have one syllable. In the second, put the six words that have two syllables. In the third, put the three words that have three syllables.

cent	Mama	Papa
valentine	center	mistake
package	fact	uniform
practicing	wrapping	Riggs
ache	cards	war

Five to Three

Splash! Splash! Kick! Kick! Faster! Faster and *faster!* Jane lifted her head to take a quick look. Then she slowed down and coasted until her fingers touched the smooth, cool wall at the end of the pool.

When she pulled herself up out of the water, Mary, the captain of the girls' swimming team, smiled at her. "I've been watching you," she said. "If you keep on practicing, you might be good enough to make the team."

Jane was so pleased that she wanted to dive right back into the pool and swim faster than ever. "Oh," she said, and her blue eyes were shining, "do you think I could?"

"Just keep on practicing and practicing," Mary answered. "Then you'll have a chance to try out for the team. So long. See you tomorrow."

Jane felt warm and happy as she hurried out to get her clothes. Wait until she told her mother and father that she had a chance to make the swimming team! Wouldn't they be proud of a daughter who was the youngest girl on the team!

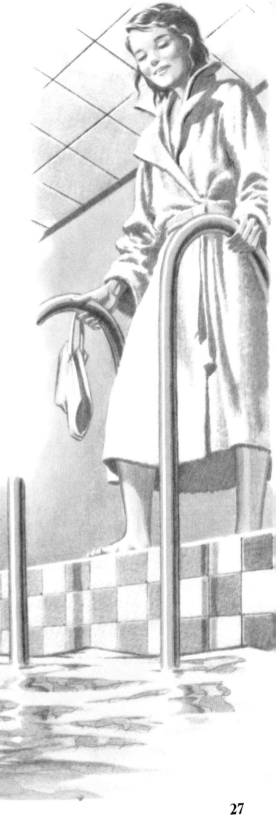

Suddenly Jane noticed the clock on the wall. Oh! It was late. She wouldn't have time now to do her homework before dinner.

"I'll get my books," she thought, as she pulled on her clothes, "and study at home tonight after dinner."

When Jane pushed open the door of the classroom, Miss Banks, her teacher, looked up from the pile of papers she was marking.

"Hello," she said. "I was just thinking about you, Jane."

Jane walked quickly past the teacher to her own desk. "I just came to get my books," she said. She didn't want to talk to Miss Banks right now.

"Jane," Miss Banks said, "I'd like to have a talk with your mother soon. Will you tell her, please?"

Jane's feelings took a long, long slide down. "Have I done something?" she asked.

Miss Banks looked tired and unhappy. "It's not what you've done. It's what you haven't done," she replied.

"You spend so much time swimming that there's no time left for studying. And if you don't start to study more, I'm afraid that you won't be able to keep up with the friends in your group. So I want to talk to your mother about it."

Jane felt her face getting hot as she stared angrily at her teacher. Miss Banks did not understand how important it was to be the youngest girl on the swimming team. "I'll tell my mother," Jane said. And she hurried out the door.

Her mother was starting to set the table for dinner when Jane came in and dropped her books on a chair.

"Hello, Jane," her mother said. "You're late. How was school?"

"Fine," Jane answered in a flat voice. She rubbed her hand over her wet hair.

"Well, you certainly don't *sound* fine!" said her mother. "What's the matter?"

"Nothing," Jane answered. Then after a moment she added, "Miss Banks wants to see you."

"She does? What about?" her mother asked as she put the plates and glasses on the table.

Jane tried not to look at her mother. "She says that I'm spending too much time swimming." Her words came faster and faster. "She says I can't keep up with my own group unless I study more."

Her mother went right on setting the table. "But why does she want to talk to me?"

Jane stopped staring down at the floor and stared at her mother. What silly questions mothers sometimes asked! "She wants to talk to you, Mother, so you'll make me stop swimming so much and study more."

Jane's mother pulled out a chair and sat down slowly. Jane could see that she was thinking hard.

Quickly, before her mother could say anything, she cried, "Mary said that if I practiced and practiced, I might make the team! Think of that!"

"Well, that would be fine, certainly," her mother replied. "But you *do* go to school to learn, you know."

Jane waited. She knew what her mother was going to say. And then she wouldn't be able to practice enough to make the swimming team!

"You know, Jane," Mother said at last, "I don't think I will go to see Miss Banks. It's your problem, not mine."

Jane's mouth dropped open. She had been so sure that her mother was going to tell her, *"No more swimmimg!"*

"But, Mother," said Jane, "I don't know what you mean. Miss Banks wants to talk to you so you will make me . . ."

Her mother stopped her. "You told me all that," she said. "But I still say it's your own problem. Unless you study more, you might fall behind your group at school.

"And of course you'd have to spend a lot more time in class than you'd be spending at the swimming pool. So you will just have to decide for yourself what you want to do. I can't decide for you, Jane, and neither can anyone else."

"But, Mother . . ." Jane tried again. Then she stopped.

"What's the use?" Jane thought. "Mother just doesn't understand how much it means to me to make the swimming team. She doesn't even care if I have to be in a group without my friends. She just tells me to decide for myself.

"Well, I don't have to decide right now. I'll keep practicing my swimming for one more week, and study hard at night."

But later that night, when Jane opened her book in her room, the words danced before her eyes. She was just too tired to study. She kicked off her shoes, undressed, and got into bed.

Jane tossed and turned. Every time she moved her legs, she imagined that they were kicking in the water. Splash! Kick! Faster and faster! She could almost smell and feel the cool water of the pool.

She thought of the warm, proud feeling she had when Mary told her she might make the team. She shut her eyes and tried hard to feel that way again, but she couldn't.

Instead, she saw herself sliding into a seat in some strange, new classroom. Two boys behind her were whispering and pointing at her and saying that she was dumb. She could swim fast, yes, but she couldn't read well at all.

Finally Jane sat up in bed. "All right," she said to herself, "I have to decide right now. Dad says it helps to list your reasons, so I will."

Jane turned on the light and climbed out of bed. She took two pieces of paper out of her desk.

At the top of one piece, Jane wrote STUDYING. Then, under that, she listed all her reasons for studying.

Studying
1. I go to school to learn.
2. I want to stay with my own group of friends.
3. I don't want people to think I'm dumb.

Jane thought about number three for a minute and then, below it, she wrote:

4. I'm not dumb.

She tapped her pencil on the desk and then added:

5. I really like to study.

Jane smiled. At the top of the second list, she wrote SWIMMING. And then she started to list the reasons why she should spend a lot of time practicing swimming.

Swimming
1. I love to swim.
2. I'd like very much to make the swimming team.
3. Swimming is good for me.

Jane looked from one list to the other. Five to three! She tried to think of more reasons why she should keep on swimming, but she couldn't.

"Well," Jane thought, "I guess I've decided! As Dad always says, 'That's a fact and that's that!' I'll have to start studying so I can keep up with my group."

Suddenly Jane felt happy again. She got into bed and fell asleep so fast that she forgot to turn off the light.

A Wise Daughter

At first it seemed to Jane that neither answer to her problem was the right one. Then, after talking with her mother, she wrote her reasons for studying in one list and her reasons for swimming in another. The lists showed that she had five reasons for studying and only three reasons for spending much of her time swimming. Knowing these facts, Jane made up her mind quickly and easily.

Suppose you were going to make two lists to help you decide between watching television and making up some schoolwork that you missed. Which reasons would you put in each list? Write the headings *Television* and *Schoolwork* and put the right numbers under each.

1. I like to watch television.
2. I won't be able to understand tomorrow's lessons unless I stay at my desk and do the work I missed.
3. I want to read the play that my group read while I was away from school.
4. The funniest television shows are on tonight.
5. I want to catch up with the rest of my class.
6. I'll learn more if I do the work I missed.

When Two Words Make One Word

Put the two underlined words together to make the word needed in the following blank. On your paper write the word that should appear in each blank.

1. Jane's <u>class</u> studied in <u>Room</u> 16. She went to her __ every morning.

2. After both hands of the clock pointed to twelve, the noon bell rang. That __ Jane practiced swimming.

3. After school, Jane's teacher told her that she should spend more time studying. Jane dreaded talking to her __.

4. When Jane went home, she tried to work on her lessons. But she was too tired to do her __.

5. Jane went to bed at her usual time, but she could not get to sleep. Long after her __, she got up and made lists to help her decide what to do.

Quiet, Please

Say the word *dumb* to yourself. At the end of this word, do you hear the sound that *b* usually stands for? No, you don't. The *b* in *dumb* is a silent letter.

On your paper write the names of the following pictures. Underline the silent letter in each name.

What the Minutes Say

We are but minutes — little things!
Each one of us has sixty wings,
With which we fly on our unseen track,
And not a minute ever comes back.

We are but minutes; use us well,
For how we are used we must one day tell.
Who uses minutes, has hours to use;
Who loses minutes, whole years must lose.

SNOWBALL FIGHT

This is a story that does not have an ending. It is about a boy who has a problem that any boy or girl might have. While you are reading the story, try to think what you would do if you were in Jim Walker's place.

Jim Walker whistled as he crossed the snow-covered field on his way to school. It was the first heavy snowfall that winter — a wet snow that would pack down hard and smooth.

Jim was thinking of all the fun he would have later, sledding with his friend Bill on the long, straight hill behind Bill's house.

Suddenly a hard snowball hit Jim on the shoulder.

Jim turned around quickly. He saw Bill coming across the field behind him. Jim made a snowball and threw it back, missing Bill by almost a foot.

"You can't play on my team if you can't throw any better than that!" laughed Bill.

"All right, how's this one?" called Jim, throwing another snowball. This time it hit Bill on the arm.

The boys kept on throwing snowballs back and forth until Jim reached the edge of the field, right next to a little stone house. He held up his hand.

"No more!" he called, grinning. "I'm safe. I win with six hits to your five."

Bill reached down for one more handful of snow, packing it into a hard, round ball.

"Don't throw that!" Jim cried. "Don't you remember what the principal said last week about throwing snowballs near houses?"

"Just one more and we'll be even!" shouted Bill, throwing as he said it.

Jim ducked as he saw the snowball coming straight at his head.

Crash! The big window on old Mrs. King's house broke into a hundred pieces!

Without stopping to think, Jim and Bill ran toward the school at the end of the block. When they were out of sight around a corner, Bill looked back to see what was happening. All was quiet. No one had appeared.

Bill let out a long, low whistle. "We're lucky nobody saw us," he said.

That afternoon the whole school was called to a meeting at three o'clock.

Jim's face turned red as he walked in and guessed what the meeting was about. Up on the stage sat old Mrs. King, talking to the principal!

Jim looked quickly at Bill, but Bill was staring steadily out the window.

When everyone was seated, Mr. Berry, the school principal, began to speak. "Is there anyone here who does not know our rule about not throwing snowballs near houses?"

No one said anything. Jim looked over at Bill again, but this time Bill was looking down at his hands.

"This morning," Mr. Berry went on, "one of you threw a snowball and broke a window in Mrs. King's house. Do you think it's fair for Mrs. King to have to pay for it when one of you broke our rule?"

"No," answered most of the children.

"Then who do you think should pay for that window?" the principal asked.

"The one who broke it!" someone called out.

"You're right," Mr. Berry agreed. "I shall expect whoever broke it to come and tell me about it. Or if anyone saw someone else break it, it's only fair for him to tell."

Jim waited in the hall for Bill. "Are you going to tell?" Jim asked when Bill came out.

"No. I didn't mean to break the window," said Bill. "Besides, I was in the field when I threw the snowball."

"But the rule says not to throw *near* houses," said Jim.

"Well, I'd have hit you instead of the window if you hadn't ducked!" said Bill, getting angry. "So it's really your fault as much as mine."

"But I told you not to throw it!" cried Jim, who was also angry by this time.

"Yes, but that was because you wanted to win the snowball fight," said Bill hotly.

"I think you should tell," said Jim.

"Well, I'm not going to. And if you do, Jim, then I'll never speak to you again!" Bill walked away angrily.

Jim stood there trying to decide what to do. If he told, he would lose his best friend, and he'd be called a tattletale. But if he didn't, Mrs. King would have to pay for the new window herself, which Jim knew wouldn't be easy for her.

What would you do if you were Jim?

Words That Belong Together

Which three of these pictures belong together?

1. 2. 3. 4.

The paper, the pencil, and the ruler should go together because all three of them are things you use in school. The nest is out of place in this group.

On your paper write the one word in each of the following groups that does not belong.

1. Teacher, principal, school, kitten
2. Splash, fault, bang, crash
3. Lazybones, steady, tattletale, scared-y-cat
4. Army, uniform, magic, gun

Unlocking Word Sounds

Suppose you had not met the words *problem* and *principal* before you saw them in *Snowball Fight*. How would you try to read them? First you should see how each new word begins.

You would see that *problem* and *principal* start with the same two letters, *pr*. *Pretty*, *prize*, and *proud* start with the same letters and the same sound.

Think of the names of the following pictures. Which name starts with the sound that *pr* stands for? Write 1, 2, 3, or 4.

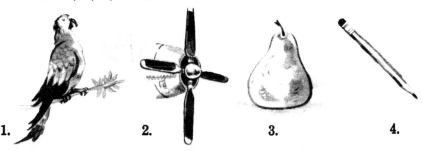

1. 2. 3. 4.

Tag-Along Trouble

Betty banged the door shut and threw down her books as she came in from school. Her mother looked up quickly.

"Lunch hour is the worst hour of the day!" Betty cried. "Sally Robinson and her crowd talk and laugh and have such a good time, and I'm always left out! This new school is just awful, Mother. I'll never have any friends here."

"Oh, yes you will, dear," Mrs. Carter answered. "Just give yourself a little more time. You shouldn't expect to feel at home in a new school after only three weeks."

"I wish that I could get to know Sally Robinson and her crowd," Betty said unhappily. "But they're always so busy having fun together that they never even notice me."

"Do you always say hello to Sally Robinson and the other girls when you get to school in the morning?" asked Mrs. Carter. "Do you try to talk with them?"

"Goodness, Mother!" sighed Betty. "I don't know what to say to those girls. I'm just a stranger in that class, and I'm sure they don't want to talk to a stranger."

Mrs. Carter shook her head and said, "You should try to talk to the girls. You'd soon find yourself feeling as much at ease with them as Polly feels with her new friends."

Polly, Betty's five-year-old sister, looked up and smiled when she heard her name. She was playing with a little girl that Betty did not know.

"You'll find some friends, Betty," said Polly. "I found one today. Her name is Ann."

"Come here, Ann," said Polly to her new little friend, who was still hugging a doll in the corner. "We can play with my sister now. You will play with us, won't you, Betty? We've been waiting for you."

"Goodness no, not that!" exclaimed Betty. "I'm going to the zoo this afternoon to see the new lion cubs."

"May we go, too?" cried Polly. "Please take us with you, Betty, please!"

Betty knew that a plain *no* would never answer a coaxer like her sister Polly, so she shouted her answer.

"No!" she exclaimed. "I don't want you tagging along everywhere I go!"

The words were no sooner out of her mouth than Betty was sorry she had said them. Her mother looked disappointed, too. "You may go to the zoo alone if you'd rather, Betty," she said quietly.

Polly slipped up to Betty and took her hand. "Please take us with you," she coaxed. "If you do, I'll give you my strawberry ice cream tonight."

Betty couldn't keep from smiling when she heard that. "Oh, all right," she sighed. "You and Ann may come with me. And you can keep your ice cream, too. I'm sorry I was so mean."

Ann and Polly chattered and laughed as they bounced along the sidewalks. At first, Betty felt lonely, because they reminded her that she had no new friends yet herself.

But by the time they came to the zoo, Betty was laughing, too, and beginning to enjoy her two little tag-alongs.

At the elephant cage, one of the elephants poked his big trunk through the bars of the cage. Polly and Ann were both scared. They hid behind Betty.

"Don't be such scared-y-cats!" Betty laughed. "Here, let's give the elephant some of these peanuts. He won't hurt you. Watch me."

The two little girls stared, their eyes growing bigger and bigger, as the elephant caught the peanuts with his waving trunk.

"Come on — you two feed him now," Betty coaxed, trying to pull the girls out from behind her back.

Ann stepped out for one second and threw a handful of peanuts toward the elephant. Then she jumped back behind Betty again.

Polly pulled Betty's hand. "You said we were going to see the lion cubs," she said. "Let's go *now*. I want to see the baby lions!"

Betty led them along to a nearby cage.

"Oh!" Ann cried. "Look at the pretty kittens!"

"They're not kittens, Ann. They're the lion cubs," laughed Betty.

"Well, they look just like kittens to me, and I want to pet them," said Ann. Before Betty knew what was going on, Ann had pulled away from her and had started to slip under the fence around the cage.

Betty was after her like a flash. She caught Ann's feet, pulling her back quickly, just as the mother lion jumped up with a roar.

On her feet again, Ann grinned, not knowing what a dangerous thing she had done. "That was fun!" she cried.

Betty didn't dare to think of what might have happened if she hadn't caught Ann in time. "We have to start home now," she said, as she led the girls away.

On the way home, Betty watched Polly and Ann laughing as they skipped along so happily together. Again she thought how lucky Polly was to have found a new friend.

Their laughter made her think of the laughter of Sally Robinson and her friends. It was laughter that Betty, so far, had not been invited to share. How she longed to feel at ease in her new school!

But Betty had always felt uncomfortable and shy around strangers. She had never known what to say to them. She sighed now, wondering if she would ever find new friends.

Suddenly Ann stopped in front of a red brick house. "This is where I live," she said. "Come on in. My mother lets us invite our friends for milk and cookies."

There was no way for Betty to know, as they were following Ann into her house, that Sally Robinson would also be there. There was no way for Betty to know that five or six other girls from her class would be there, too.

But there they were, with friends of their own age. And here she was, with these two little tag-along girls that didn't even know enough to stay out of the lions' cage! What would they think of her, playing with babies?

Betty felt so awful that she wished she could drop through the floor and disappear!

But little Ann didn't even notice that there was anything wrong. She ran over to Sally Robinson and gave her a hug. "I've been to the zoo, Sis!" she cried. "What fun we had! Polly's big sister took us to see the lion cubs."

"Oh, Betty," said Sally, "how did you like those lion cubs? Everyone's been talking about them! Just before you came in, we were making plans to go and see them soon ourselves."

Sally's warm smile and her pleasant voice helped Betty to forget her shyness. She was so pleased and excited about Sally's friendliness toward her that she almost tripped over her words as she answered.

"Oh, the cubs were lots of fun!" Betty said eagerly. "I wouldn't even mind going back to see them again myself."

"Why don't you come with us when we go?" asked Sally. "We're going to have a picnic at the zoo."

"That's a good idea! You can come along with us!" cried one of the other girls. They were all looking at Betty and smiling in the nicest way.

Betty could hardly believe her ears. The girls from her class were inviting her to go to the zoo with them! She was making new friends at last! Her heart sang with happiness as she said, "Why, thanks. I would love to go with you."

When the two little girls ran off to the kitchen to eat, Sally turned to Betty. "It was awfully nice of you to take my little sister to the zoo," she said. "She's the worst tag-along you've ever seen. I can never go *anywhere* alone!"

"Oh, I know what a bother tag-alongs can be," said Betty. "Remember, I have one, too!"

But to herself, Betty was saying, "My tag-along sister helped me make some friends at last. I think I'll give Polly my ice cream tonight!"

She Might Have Been Disappointed

Betty wanted to go to the zoo by herself. She thought that taking Polly and Ann would be an awful bother and no fun. What would Betty have missed if she had decided not to take the little tag-alongs with her? Write three numbers.

1. Laughing and talking on the way to the zoo
2. Feeding the elephants
3. Seeing the lion cubs
4. Making friends with Sally Robinson
5. Being invited to the zoo again

Bright Lights on Words

Suppose you knew the word *light*, but you had not met the word *bright*. Knowing the sound of *ight* in *light* would help you to read the word *bright*. The words *light* and *bright* rhyme with each other.

Some other pairs of rhyming words are *bar* and *car*, *shy* and *sigh*, *jokes* and *coax*, *worst* and *first*, *laughter* and *after*.

The following rhyme tells what Polly and her mother said to each other at bedtime. All the words that belong in the blanks rhyme with *bright*.

"Your room is too bright;
I'll turn out your l__.
I hope you sleep t__.
My Polly, good n__."

"Please, Mama, you m__
Leave one little l__.
A room that's not br__
Gives me such a fr__."

"There's no need for fr__
If I hug you t__.
Now is it all r__
To turn off the l__?"

"Well, Mama, all r__.
The dark isn't qu__
So scary at n__
When you hold me t__."

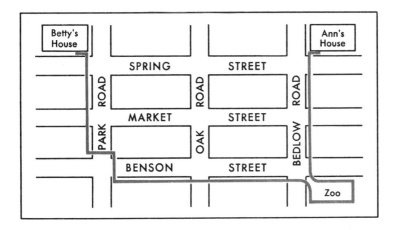

Where Did It Happen?

The red line on this map shows where Betty and the two little girls walked. If you will read the map carefully, you will know what words should appear in the following blanks. Write the words on your paper.

1. Betty's house is on the corner of __ Road and __ Street.
2. The zoo is on the corner of __ Street and __ Road.
3. To get to the zoo, Betty, Polly, and Ann first walked two blocks on __ Road.
4. The first street which the girls crossed after leaving Betty's house was __ Street.
5. On their way to the zoo, they had to cross two streets at the corner of __ Road and __ Street.
6. After they had left the zoo, the girls walked two blocks on __ Road.
7. Then they reached Ann's house, which is on the corner of __ Street and __ Road.

Mr. Nobody

I know a funny little man,
As quiet as a mouse,
Who does the mischief that is done
In everybody's house!
There's no one ever sees his face,
And yet we all agree
That every plate we break was cracked
By Mr. Nobody.

'Tis he who always tears our books,
Who leaves the door ajar.
He pulls the buttons from our shirts,
And scatters pins afar.
That squeaking door will always squeak
For, prithee, don't you see,
We leave the oiling to be done
By Mr. Nobody.

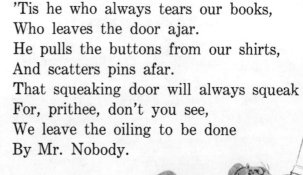

He puts damp wood upon the fire,
So kettles cannot boil;
His are the feet that bring in mud,
And all the carpets soil.
The papers always are mislaid.
Who had them last? Yes, he.
There's no one tosses them about
But Mr. Nobody.

The finger-marks upon the door
By none of us are made;
We never leave the shades pulled up
To let the curtains fade.
The ink we never spill, the boots
That lying round you see —
They're not our boots; they all belong
To Mr. Nobody.

LOOKING BACK AND REMEMBERING

The Problems You Have Read About

Write the name of the story that tells about each problem.

1. A girl had to choose between keeping up with her schoolwork and making the swimming team.
2. A boy who loved baseball felt that he could never be on a team.
3. A girl from another country worked hard to learn American ways.
4. A boy could not decide whether he should tattle on his friend.
5. A shy girl was afraid that she would never have any friends at her new school.

The Words You Have Read

Answer the questions about each rhyme.

Johnny hardly dared to dream
That he could make the baseball __.

1. What word is needed to finish the rhyme?
2. What is the only two-syllable word in the second line?
3. In this rhyme, what does *dream* mean?
    a. Thoughts, pictures, or feelings which come during sleep
    b. To imagine while awake

Oh, how Anya's eyes did shine
At the thought of baking a __.

1. What word is needed to finish the rhyme?
2. Which word starts with the same sound that *shoe* starts with?
3. Which seven-letter word has one syllable?

Betty said, "I think it's wrong
For little girls to tag ___."

1. What word is needed to finish the rhyme?
2. What word begins with a silent letter?
3. What word ends with a silent letter?

The Sound at the End

The letter *t* is at the end of the first row of pictures. The name of one picture in that row *ends* with the sound *t* stands for. Find that picture and write the name of it on your paper.

Follow these same steps with the letters and pictures in the following rows.

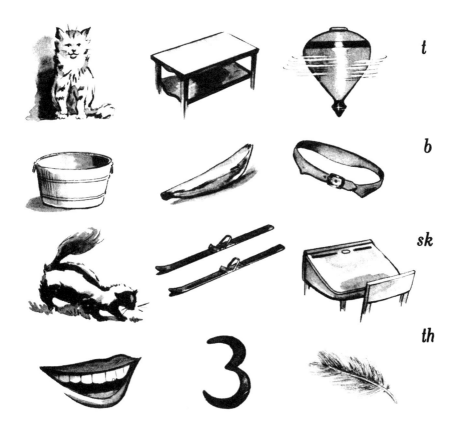

GOOD MANNERS MAY
IN SEVEN WORDS BE FOUND.
FORGET YOURSELF
AND THINK OF THOSE AROUND.

Pulling Together

Letters and Sounds

At the end of this book is a wordbook which gives the meaning of many new words in the stories. Next to each listed word is a second spelling. From it you can learn how the word is said. Let's see how it works.

First, say these words: *ate, hat, far, fall.* What letter has a different sound in each word?

Now look at those words with their respellings:

ate \\'āt\\   hat \\'hat\\   far \\'fär\\   fall \\'fȯl\\

In the first respelling, the ā stands for the sound of the letter *a* in *ate.* You can quickly see what stands for the sound of *a* in *hat, far,* and *fall.*

Below is a Key to Sounds, which you will also find on page 282. All the tricky parts of a respelling are listed in the key. There are key words to help you understand each sound. Say the key words that show the sound that u̇ stands for. How can you tell what sound ȯi stands for?

Practice using the key, and you will soon know all the sounds shown in the respellings of the wordbook.

Key to Sounds

ā	ate, they	ī	mile, lying	ch	chair
a	hat, land	i	mill, indeed, here	l	little
ä	far, father, got	ō	go, arrow	n	seven
au̇	out, how	ȯ	horn, dog, fall, paw	ng	ring
ē	meet, begin, easy	ȯi	oil, toy	r	letter
e	met, care	ü	blue, too, used \\'yüzd\\	sh	wish
		u̇	put, good, poor	th	thank
		ə	ago, up, perhaps	th	than
			her, hurt, bird	zh	garage

Pennies for Joy

"Will was joking, wasn't he?" asked Betsy, looking at the ten pennies on the table.

"Sure," Ben nodded, agreeing with his sister. "Will didn't mean it."

Their mother smiled as she picked up the dishes Will had left when he hurried off to work. "Oh, but I think he *did* mean it!" she said. "There are the ten pennies to *prove* it!"

Then she marched off to the kitchen, leaving her son and daughter staring at each other.

When he had first finished school and had started to work, Ben and Betsy's big brother had generally been nice about giving them spending money. But lately, he had been acting strange about it.

When Ben asked Will for a nickel to buy a candy bar, Will would say, "Where's the nickel I gave you yesterday?" And once he was even cross with Betsy when she asked for money two times in one day.

So Ben had thought of an idea. They would ask Will to give them a weekly allowance of fifty cents every Saturday. Then they could spend it any way they pleased, without being reminded of how much they had spent the day before.

Since today was Saturday, they had told Will about Ben's idea for a weekly allowance. Then they asked him whether they could have the first two half dollars.

For a minute, Will just stared at them. Then he said, "How do I know you wouldn't waste the allowance?"

"We can prove we won't waste it if you just give us a chance," Ben coaxed.

Then Will did a strange thing. He took ten pennies out of his pocket and laid them on the table.

"O.K.," he said, "I'll try you out. We'll call these pennies 'joy pennies.' If you can make five people happy by the way you spend them, I'll let you have the allowance!"

Ben and Betsy ate their breakfast silently, trying not to feel too disappointed.

"Ten pennies to make five people happy!" said Ben at last. "Why, just one candy bar costs a whole nickel!"

"Say, Ben!" cried Betsy suddenly. "I know how we can make somebody happy with a penny! We can buy a licorice stick for old Mr. Bell. He just loves licorice."

Ben shook his head. "You can't make a person happy just by giving him a licorice stick," he said.

"It's not only the licorice stick," said Betsy. "Don't you think our coming to visit him would make him happy, too?"

Ben's eyes were beginning to brighten. "Well, maybe it would, at that! And I could show him the new kite I made."

When they rapped at his door, old Mr. Bell was even happier to see them than they had expected. "Come in!" he cried. "Well, well, where did you get that fine red kite?"

"I made it," Ben answered proudly.

Betsy got out the licorice stick, and Mr. Bell cut it into three pieces, saying they must help him eat it.

Mr. Bell was so happy to have them visit him that they stayed longer than they had planned. And on their way home, Betsy said, "We *did* make him happy, didn't we, Ben?"

Just then, someone behind them called out, "Hey, Ben! Wait! I want to see your new kite!" Then little Sonny Banks came running up.

"Say, Ben, that's the best kite I ever saw!" cried Sonny. "I wish I had one like it."

"You could make yourself one," said Betsy. "Ben made his, and it only cost a penny. He used some sticks that he found in the back yard, and Mother gave him the string. Then Mr. Jackson let him buy some wrapping paper for a penny."

"But I couldn't make it by myself," said Sonny, "and my mother says I can't have any more pennies until next week."

Ben and Betsy looked at each other and laughed.

Then Ben said, "We have a penny, Sonny. We'll buy the paper, and I'll help you make the kite. How would that be?"

"Will you *really*, Ben?" cried Sonny. "And will it be just like yours?"

The new kite did turn out just like Ben's. It was a fine kite, and Sonny was flying it happily when they left him and started home.

As they walked along, they passed the post office.

"You know," said Betsy, "if stamps were only a penny each instead of three cents, we could write letters to our two grandmothers. Letters would make both of them happy."

"Say! I know how we can write to our grandmothers for only two cents each instead of three!" cried Ben. "We can buy some of those postal cards that cost two cents each at the post office. You don't have to put any stamps on them!"

"And we can write very tiny," Betsy agreed, "and say a lot. Then we'll still have four cents left to make one more person happy."

But it was a strange thing about those last four pennies. They just didn't seem to want to be spent!

Ben and Betsy kept thinking about it on their way home, after mailing their postal cards. They thought about it while they ate their lunch. And they were still thinking about it when lunch was over and they started to go outside.

"Hey, Ben!" called Betsy. "Look at the stray dog on our porch! I wonder where he came from!"

Ben walked over and patted the thin, hungry-looking dog.

"Poor old fellow," Ben said. "I bet he hasn't eaten anything for days! Let's ask Mother if we can fix up a box for him behind the house."

Their mother gave them an old cushion, a blanket, and a box. Then Ben said, "May we feed him, Mother?"

"You just ate all the meat there was left," Mother said. "But I'll be buying more at the market later. Why don't you mix up some bread with a few leftover vegetables to feed him in the meantime?"

The dog quickly ate all the scraps they gave him and then looked up hopefully for more.

"Oh, Ben, this is awful!" said Betsy. "You can tell that he's still hungry. I wish we had some meat to give him." .

Ben shook his head sadly, looking down at the dog and thinking how terrible it would be to feel that hungry.

Then he said to Betsy, "Pete says Mr. Jackson sells him scraps for his dog. But Betsy, we're supposed to make some *person* happy with those pennies we have left!"

Betsy nodded, leaning over to pat the hungry dog.

Suddenly, Ben said, "Oh, come on, Betsy! Let's go see what we can get at Jackson's for four cents!"

Mr. Jackson asked lots of questions about their stray dog as he put the meat scraps in a paper bag. "That will be a nickel," he said, handing the bag to Ben.

"Oh!" cried Betsy. "We only have four cents! Can't we just take four cents worth?"

At that, Mr. Jackson smiled and said, "Oh, well, it will be all right this time."

On the way home, Ben said, "I think it's O.K. about our spending the four pennies to feed the stray dog, Betsy. But since I've been thinking about it, I'm afraid Will's going to be disappointed with the way we spent our other pennies."

"Why?" asked Betsy.

"Because we didn't really make the people happy just by spending the pennies on them. Mr. Bell was happy because we came to see him, and Sonny was happy because I helped him make the kite. See what I mean?"

That night they told Will they were all mixed up about the pennies they had spent.

"But it wasn't really our fault," said Betsy. "We knew the stray dog wasn't a person, but he was so awfully hungry!"

"Suppose we call him a 'dog person,'" Will said with a grin. "And didn't it make you and Ben happier to see him eat?"

"Sure!" Ben broke in. "I'd hate to be hungry like that!"

"Right!" said Will. "And besides, you made *me* happy by proving you wouldn't waste the allowance you asked for. So counting you and Betsy and me, the ten pennies made seven people and one dog happy!"

"Then it doesn't matter that we did something besides spending a penny on Sonny and Mr. Bell?" Ben asked.

"You bet it matters!" said Will. "If you aren't nice to people, spending money on them won't make them happy. I'm glad you proved that to yourselves. Now close your eyes and hold out your hands."

Ben and Betsy felt something round and hard placed in their hands.

"Oh, thanks!" cried Ben. "Boy, am I glad we learned how to spend money! If we made seven people happy with ten cents, there's no telling *what* we'll be able to do with fifty cents every week!"

An Allowance Well Spent

Which of these things did Mr. Bell enjoy more? Write the number on your paper.

1. The licorice stick
2. The visit from Ben and Betsy

Which of these things meant more to Sonny Banks?

1. The penny's worth of paper for his kite
2. Ben's help in making the kite

Which of these things are worth more to a person than money?

1. Kindness and thoughtfulness
2. Licorice sticks and kites

When One More Letter Makes a New Word

If you write the letter *s* before the word *team*, you have the word *steam*. What letter is needed before each of these words to make the name of the picture beside it? Write the letters on your paper.

lock

rain

tool

wing

What Does the Key Unlock?

On the first page of your wordbook (page 282) you will find a Key to Sounds. This key will help you to say the words in the wordbook. Four of the vowel letters listed have straight lines over them: ā, ē, ī, ō. These stand for the long vowel sounds, as in the words *ate*, *meet*, *mile*, and *go*.

The vowel letters that have no marks over them (a, e, i) stand for the short vowel sounds, as in the words *at*, *met*, and *mill*. The short sound of *o*, as in *got*, is shown by ä.

On your paper write the name of each picture above. After each name show whether the vowel sound is long or short (ā, a, ē, e, ī, i, ō, or ä).

Write the words below in which you hear long vowel sounds. Then write the words in which you hear short vowel sounds.

bet	postal	nickel	scrap	cost
stray	curved	problem	team	shy

In which one of these words do you hear the long sound of *a*? Write the word on your paper.

mix	rhyme	cushion	prove	hey

Dog to Be Proud Of

Billy really loved his dog Pep. But he could see, as they walked along with Tom and his fine dog, that Pep wasn't as handsome as he might be. And Billy could tell that Tom saw it, too.

That was the worst thing about Tom. He made you mad, the way he saw the things you didn't want him to, like the patches on your clothes. He saw the way your dog's ears hung down when they should point up straight.

"Hey! What kind of dog do you call *that?*" he had asked Billy as soon as they met that morning.

"He's just a dog," Billy answered. "But he's a good, friendly dog. What kind of dog do you have?"

"A bulldog," Tom replied proudly. "He's a fine show dog. Say, isn't your funny dog supposed to hold his ears up?"

"I don't know," Billy said. "His ears look all right to me." But then he looked at Pep unhappily.

Pep seemed to know that he wasn't as good as Tom thought he should be. He crawled to Billy and then got up and ran around and around in circles, barking. Billy noticed that his dog was limping.

"He's been fighting again," he said to himself. In fact, when he stopped to think about it, Pep fought quite a lot for a dog who was so friendly.

"My dog has a good name," Tom said importantly. "It's Torrance the Third. I'm taking Torrance to the doctor. He's going to have some shots."

"Well," said Billy, "I'll walk along with you, if you like."

As they walked along, he tried to think of some stories he could tell Tom about Pep. He wasn't making excuses for the way Pep looked. But he did want Tom to understand that Pep was a very special dog, even if his ears did hang down.

He told Tom how easy it had been to train Pep to carry a pair of slippers or a newspaper in his mouth. He told about Pep's way of sitting up in the corner of the kitchen when he wanted to be fed.

Then Billy told Tom how Pep liked to ride in the car, looking out the window to see what they had left behind.

But all the while, he felt that Tom wasn't really listening. Tom had a show dog — a dog whose ears stood up — a dog important enough to have shots.

When they arrived at the animal hospital, Billy walked slowly up the steps behind Tom and Torrance the Third.

The doctor smiled at them. He was a pleasant man in a white coat. He put Torrance the Third on a high table and looked at him. Then he sent him into another room to get his shots.

While the boys were waiting for Torrance to come back, the doctor noticed that Pep was limping.

"What's the matter with your dog?" he asked Billy.

"I guess he's been in a fight," said Billy. "Pep likes to fight."

"Come here," the doctor said to Pep.

Pep walked over to him and held up his hurt foot.

The doctor looked at it carefully to find out what was causing Pep to limp. Then he patted Pep on one of his hanging ears and said, "No wonder you were limping, little Pep. This paw has a foxtail in it."

He took a small tool and pulled out the sharp point of grass. "Foxtails are a kind of grass with sharply pointed stickers. And when a foxtail gets caught in a dog's paw, it can cut him badly and cause a lot of pain."

When Torrance the Third came out from the other room, Pep's foot was neatly tied up. He was still limping, but he looked happy now, and ready to go home.

One day a few weeks later, Pep strayed away from home.

Billy searched for him for hours, but no one had seen his little dog.

At last Billy's mother said, "Pep could have been hit by a car, Billy. Why don't you go down to the animal hospital and ask whether they know anything about him?"

And so, trembling with fear, Billy went to see the animal doctor. It was a long, hot walk, halfway across the city. When he got there, the doctor was sitting in his office, and Billy went in and asked him whether he had seen Pep.

The doctor smiled at him. "I remember you," he said. "Your dog had a foxtail in his paw a few weeks ago, didn't he?"

"Oh, yes, that's my dog. But now he's wandered away," said Billy sorrowfully. "I can't find him anywhere. I thought if he'd been hit by a car, he might have been brought here."

"He hasn't been hit by a car," the doctor said, "but I do know where he is." Opening a door, he called, "Here, Pep!"

In answer to the call, a lively bundle of fur raced into the room and jumped at Billy.

"What are you doing here?" cried Billy, hugging his dog.

Then the doctor explained. "This morning I heard a dog scratching at the door. So I opened it, and there stood Pep, holding up his paw and crying as if he were in pain.

"I took him in and found that there was another foxtail in his paw that was hurting him. After I took it out, I started wondering how to find you again. I was just thinking about it when you walked in."

"Boy, am I glad to get Pep back!" Billy cried. He just kept hugging Pep, and Pep kept licking his hands, as if they had been away from each other for years instead of hours.

"You should be," said the doctor. "He is a very smart dog. He knows just where to go when he's in trouble, which is more than some people do."

"How can I pay you?" Billy remembered. "I don't have any money with me, but I will ask my father to send you some. Will that be all right?"

But the doctor shook his head. "This won't cost you a cent," he said. "Pep came to me as a friend and asked me to help him. I helped him just as a friend might do."

Soon Pep and Billy were out on the sidewalk, walking home. Billy was so proud of Pep that he went back by way of Tom's house. He just had to tell Tom what a smart thing Pep had done.

When Billy finished talking to him, Tom said with a sigh, "I wish Torrance were as smart as that, but he just isn't."

Billy said quickly, "Well, Tom, Torrance is a very handsome dog, and he is a fine bulldog."

But this time, he was saying it to make Tom feel better. Billy had just found out something important. Pep was a dog to be proud of — the doctor had said so.

The Thing to Say

In the beginning of the story *Dog to Be Proud Of*, Tom said some unkind things about Pep and boasted about Torrance. At the end of the story, Tom said he wished that Torrance were as smart as Pep. Write your answers to these questions:

1. How did Billy feel about the unkind things Tom said?
2. How did Billy feel when Tom praised Pep?
3. Do you think that Billy liked Tom better at the beginning of the story or at the end of the story? Why?

The Better Dog

Tom was proud of Torrance because Torrance was handsome. Billy was proud of his dog Pep because Pep was smart. Which boy do you think had better reason to be proud of his dog? Why? Write your answer.

If you were choosing a dog for yourself, would you rather have one like Torrance the Third or one like Pep? Why? Write your reasons.

The Better Word

On your paper write the word for each blank.

1. Even though Pep was usually a __ (friendly, unfriendly) dog, he sometimes fought.
2. "Mother, I can't find Pep," Billy said __. (sorrowfully, boastfully)
3. Billy was breathless after he ran __ (slowly, quickly) up the steps of the animal hospital.
4. "I never need to make excuses for Pep," Billy said __. (proudly, beautifully)

Cat to Be Proud Of

If you liked the story of Billy's smart dog Pep, maybe you will also like the following rhyme about a clever cat. If you will remember the sound of *at*, you can decide what word should appear at the end of each line.

Blackie the Bat
Lifted his h__
To proud Mrs. C__,
Who sat on a m__.

He said, "Mrs. C__,
You're getting too f__.
I'm betting you th__
You can't catch a r__."

Proud Mrs. C__
Said, "Bet me your h__."

Then Rosie the R__
Crawled too near the m__.
Life is like th__.

Now proud Mrs. C__
Has put on more f__
And wears a new h__.

The Long and Short of It

Write the following words in three lists. In the first list put the words in which you hear the short sound of *a* (a). In the second list put the words in which you hear the long sound of *a* (ā). In the third list put the words in which *a* is a silent letter.

rap	praise	pain
ache	blank	fear
mad	boast	map

Don't Say It

Dick stood at one end of the baseball field by the old bag which was home plate. The sun felt good on his back. He pushed up his cap and grinned at Joe. "Pitch it!" he yelled. "I can hit anything today!"

The ball curved toward the right, and so Dick didn't even bother to swing at it. "Ball!" he shouted, throwing down his bat and running to get the ball out of the bushes.

When he tossed the ball back to Joe, he called to him, "Throw it straight, can't you?"

This time, the ball went to the left of home plate and Dick had to climb a fence to get it.

The third time he had to chase a ball, he began to feel hot and angry. His shirt was sticking to his back, and he had scratched his knee on the fence.

"Look!" he called to Joe. "Can't you *see* home plate?"

"I'm *trying* to throw the ball straight," Joe shouted back. "Here — hit this one."

But the ball went over the fence again.

"You get it yourself this time!" Dick shouted angrily. "You couldn't throw a straight ball if you had a ruler!"

Joe climbed over the fence and picked up the ball. He tossed it back to Dick. Then he pushed through the bushes toward the path.

"Hey, Joe! Where are you going?" Dick shouted.

"I'm going home. I don't want to play with you," Joe called, without turning around.

"Who cares?" Dick called after him. But he did care. For this was the first sunshiny Saturday in a month, and now he had no one to play with. He pounded his bat against the ground. There was nothing to do but go home.

Dick stamped up the steps, banging the door behind him. His mother looked up and asked, "Did you forget something?"

"No!" Dick said, almost shouting at her. Then he told her how he had made Joe mad.

"And now Joe's angry and you are, too," his mother said. "So telling him he couldn't throw straight didn't do either one of you any good, did it?"

Dick felt his neck and his face starting to get hot again. It wasn't fair for his mother to blame him because Joe wouldn't play. He said angrily, "You just don't understand, Mother. He couldn't throw *one* straight ball. I *had* to tell him."

"Let's go sit on the side porch," his mother said. "I want to tell you a story about Abraham Lincoln."

It was pleasant and cool on the porch. Dick dropped down in the porch swing. He pushed both his feet against the floor and made the swing go back and forth, back and forth, creak-creak, creak-creak.

He didn't want to sit here on the porch and listen to a story about some old President. He wanted to play baseball.

His mother started to talk in her sweet, low voice.

"When Lincoln was a young man," she began, "he often criticized people. He would tell his friends when he thought they had done wrong. He even wrote letters to other people, saying that they had done or said the wrong thing.

"Lincoln made many people angry when he criticized them. People just don't like to be told when they have done something wrong."

Dick stopped swinging long enough to say, "I don't like to be told, but you tell me."

"That's true, of course," his mother agreed. "I do criticize you sometimes. But you see, Dick, there are two kinds of criticism. One kind of criticism really helps you to do better, but the other kind just hurts you and causes a lot of trouble.

"When I criticize you for doing something wrong, I try at the same time to tell you how to do it right. And I never criticize you if I think you've done your best. Do you see?"

"Maybe," Dick replied.

"Well, years later Lincoln became President of the United States," his mother went on. "By that time, he had learned not to criticize anyone unless it would do some good.

"While he was President, a terrible war started in this country between the Southern states and the states of the North. Lincoln hated the war; he wanted his Northern generals to do everything they could to end it quickly.

"But some of his generals were not as wise as Lincoln. They made bad mistakes. Let me tell you about one of those mistakes and what Lincoln did about it.

"The army from the South had fought its way up into the North. Lincoln's general in that part of the country was a man named Meade.

"Meade knew that it was important for him to stop the Southern army. For three days his men fought hard.

"It was in the middle of the summer. The heat, there at Gettysburg, was terrible, but not so terrible as the roaring of the guns. And even more terrible were the cries of the men who were hurt."

"Did General Meade stop the soldiers from the South?" Dick asked. He was sitting up straight, now, and listening to every word.

"Yes, he stopped them," his mother answered. "After those three days of fighting at Gettysburg, the Southern army finally had to retreat.

73

"Many of its brave soldiers had been killed, and those who were still alive were too tired to fight any more.

"It had started to rain. The retreat of those Southern soldiers from Gettysburg was made even harder by the terrible downpour."

"Did they get away from Gettysburg all right?" Dick asked.

"They were stopped by a wide river," his mother replied. "There was no bridge, and the tired soldiers could not get across through the deep, swift water. With General Meade and his army behind them, and the river in front of them, they were trapped."

Dick leaned forward. "Boy, that was a good chance for the Northern army to knock out the Southern army," he said.

"Yes," replied his mother. "Lincoln thought so, too. And he knew that if the Northern army captured the Southern army, the war would be over at once. Then there would be no more killing and no more sorrow.

"The men could go back to their homes and their families again. And after a while, all the states could live together in peace again, as they had lived before the war.

"So Lincoln sent word to General Meade, saying that he should drive forward at once to attack and capture the retreating Southern army."

"Good for him!" cried Dick.

"But General Meade did not attack," his mother went on. "Instead, he talked with all his top officers about what he should do. He just kept talking and talking.

"While he was talking, the rain stopped and the waters of the river started going down. After a few days, the river was low enough for the soldiers to cross it safely, and the whole Southern army got away.

"Lincoln was very angry. He sat right down and wrote Meade a letter. He told him that, by not attacking, he had missed a chance to bring peace to his country. He said that, because of Meade's mistake, the war might go on for years."

"Did the letter make the general mad?" Dick asked.

"General Meade never saw the letter," his mother replied. "Lincoln didn't send it. Maybe he began to wonder if the letter would do any good, since it was too late to capture the Southern army.

"And perhaps he thought the General had done the best he could at the time. Lincoln was a wise and a good man. I think he knew that if a person has done his best, criticism hurts instead of helps."

When his mother stopped talking, Dick pushed the swing back and forth, back and forth. He was thinking very hard.

"Lincoln was a smart man, all right," Dick said to himself. "If he had criticized General Meade, it might have made him mad, the way I made my pal Joe mad. Then he might have said he wouldn't lead the soldiers any more."

Dick jumped up. "I'll go find Joe," he said, "and say I'm sorry. Then I'll show him how to pitch a ball straight."

It's Not What You Say; It's the Way You Say It

At the end of the story, Dick decided that he would teach his friend Joe how to throw straight. In order to be a good teacher, Dick must remember not to give Joe unkind criticism for his bad pitches. Instead, he should give Joe praise for his good pitches.

If you were Joe, which of the following things would you like to hear Dick say to you? Write *a* or *b* for each number.

1. a. That pitch was closer to home plate than your last throw.
    b. You're still not throwing the ball over home plate.

2. a. You're throwing to the left again after only three straight pitches.
    b. You threw three good, straight ones before pitching too far to the left.

3. a. Won't you ever learn not to throw the ball over my head?
    b. Would you try to throw the ball lower next time?

4. a. Today half of your pitches were good.
    b. Today half of your pitches were terrible.

Saying It in an Outline

The story *Don't Say It* can be divided into three parts. The first part tells how the ball game ended because Dick had criticized Joe. The second part tells about President Lincoln and General Meade. The third part tells what Dick decided to do about playing ball with Joe.

If you were making an outline of *Don't Say It*, you would use three headings to show the three parts of the story. Which of the following sentences would you choose for each heading? Write *a* or *b* for each number.

    I. **a.** Dick and his pal Joe played ball.

        b. Dick criticized Joe unkindly.

   II. **a.** Lincoln decided not to criticize Meade.

        b. Lincoln blamed Meade because he did not capture the army of the Southern states.

  III. **a.** Dick was interested in his mother's story about the fighting at Gettysburg.

        b. Dick decided to stop criticizing Joe and to help Joe learn to pitch.

When Vowels Get Together

In the word *creak, e* and *a* appear together. The *e* stands for the *long e* sound; the *a* is silent. In the word *praise, a* and *i* appear together. The *a* stands for the *long a* sound; the *i* is silent. When two vowels appear together in a syllable, they usually stand for the long sound of the first vowel.

On your paper write the two vowels needed in each blank to make a word with the meaning that follows.

    1. r__n   water from the clouds

    2. M__de   Lincoln's general

    3. repl__d   answered

    4. retr__t   to go back

    5. p__n   ache

    6. cr__m   the fatty part of milk

    7. thr__t   neck

    8. p__ceful quiet

Big Brother

Peter slipped out of bed. It was still dark outside, but he knew he must hurry. As he pulled on his clothes, he heard the chuff-chuff of the circus train on the railroad siding across the cornfield.

He listened at the door a moment before tiptoeing out into the shadowy hallway. The house was quiet and peaceful, so he moved carefully down the stairs on his bare feet.

Just before he reached the last step, he thought he heard a floor board creak in Jimmy's room.

Peter frowned, fearful that his little brother might have awakened. Then he stood there, listening and thinking, "I hope Jimmy doesn't wake up now. This is one time I just *won't* have him tagging along."

There was no other sound from Jimmy's room, so Peter tiptoed on down the hall to the back door. There he listened again before he eased the door open and slipped outside.

Even in the darkness, Peter could see the shape of the oak trees against the moonless sky. The silvery stars crowding the sky reminded him of the shiny pins that crowded his mother's blue pincushion.

For a moment the deep, lonesome ache for his mother made him want to cry.

Just then the back door creaked. Without turning to see why, Peter started running across the yard toward the cornfield. "I guess I didn't close the door tightly," he said to himself. "I'm sure Jimmy didn't hear me get up."

It made him unhappy and angry deep inside just to think about Jimmy.

When their mother had to go away to the hospital because she was sick, she had hugged Peter tightly. "Take care of Jimmy for me," she had said.

But Jimmy didn't like being taken care of. He was little and funny, and he "showed off" all the time. He made their aunts and uncles laugh, and they called him a little dear. They didn't even look at Peter.

That was bad enough. But what was even worse was the way Jimmy was always causing trouble. Then Peter would get blamed for Jimmy's mistakes.

"You're a big boy, so you should take better care of your brother," his grandmother would say. "You can't blame Jimmy. He's just a little fellow."

Then she would smile and pat Jimmy on the head. And he would make a funny face at Peter. Everyone would laugh — everyone, that is, but Peter.

Peter stepped carefully into the shadowy little path between the rows of tall, fresh corn.

The earth felt cool and pleasant under his bare feet. The peaceful stillness of the early-morning countryside was broken only by the rustle of the corn, bowing in the wind.

It was exciting and a bit scary, too, to be out all alone before daylight. Peter walked along, forgetting about Jimmy.

Soon he could hear the voices of men calling to one another. The engine kept going chuff-chuff, chuff-chuff. Then it gave a long, tired ssshhh.

Peter climbed the fence at the edge of the cornfield and took a deep, happy breath.

The circus train was standing, as it did every year, on the railroad siding across the road from the cornfield.

It was still too dark to see the faces of the men walking near the train. But the swinging lanterns in their hands dropped moving pools of yellow light on the ground all around their feet.

A truck came slowly along the country road, poking its long fingers of light before it. The truck backed up to a boxcar just across the road.

Peter blinked his eyes in the sudden light. Then the driver turned out the lights of the truck, and the darkness closed in again, broken only by the swinging lanterns.

Peter heard the door of the boxcar slide back, and he shivered happily at the sound of a low, uneasy growl. A man shouted, "Watch it!" as four other men unloaded one of the heavy animal cages from the boxcar onto the truck.

Suddenly a hand touched Peter's arm, and he jumped, so scared that he almost yelled.

It was Jimmy. "Hey," he whispered, "have they unloaded the lions yet?"

Peter grabbed his brother by both of his shoulders and shook him. "Why do you always have to tag along after me? *Go home!*" he whispered angrily.

Jimmy pulled himself free and peered across the road. "What's in that cage on the truck?" he asked. "A lion?"

"Go *home*, I said," Peter whispered again, even though he knew it was hopeless.

Instead of answering him, Jimmy said, "I'm going across the road so I can see better."

"Oh, no you're not!" Peter objected. "That's too close." He grabbed Jimmy's arm, but Jimmy slipped away from him and scampered across the road.

"If you get into trouble, don't expect *me* to come help you!" Peter whispered after him. He leaned back against the tree. There was just no use trying to take care of his little brother.

It wasn't his fault that Jimmy had come, but he would get blamed for it, anyway.

Soon the headlights on the truck went on again. Peter could see Jimmy's curly head sticking up above the thick weeds near the train. Then the truck turned around and moved slowly off down the road.

The pincushion sky was fading now, from blue to gray. It was becoming light enough for Peter to see the outlines of the brightly colored posters on the sides of the boxcars. One by one, the men turned off their lanterns.

Peter peered up at the sky for a moment. The stars, now, were only far-away pinpoints of light. Suddenly he heard a frightened squeal.

Peter jumped up and stared across the road. A man as tall as a giant had grabbed Jimmy and was holding him in the air, high above his head.

"Peter! Peter!" Jimmy cried. His voice was choked with fear.

For a moment Peter was too frightened to move. Then he raced across the road and threw himself at the giant's leg. "Stop!" he yelled. "You let my brother go!"

The giant chuckled. "You let *me* go, sonny," he said in a deep voice.

Peter fought with all his might, beating wildly against the giant's leg with his hands and his bare feet. "Put him down!" he shouted, "or I'll — I'll —" The words choked in his throat.

"Stop that!" warned the giant. Then he lowered Jimmy to the ground.

Peter grabbed hold of his brother and pulled him away. Jimmy hung onto Peter and began to cry.

"Here, here," the big man said, "I didn't mean to scare you, little boy. I was only playing when I picked you up."

Jimmy was sobbing with his face against Peter's arm.

Feeling his little brother so close to him, shaking with fear, made Peter feel big and strong. He even felt strong enough to fight a real, live giant.

"It's all right, Jimmy," he said. "The man said he didn't mean to scare you. He was only playing."

"But he's so big," Jimmy sobbed.

The man laughed, deep in his throat. "Of course I'm big," he said. "I'm the Tall Man in the circus."

The giant looked just like any other man, except that he was as tall as a giraffe. He turned away, now, chuckling again to himself.

"I'm sorry if I frightened you, sonny," he said. "But don't be mad. Come and see me in the sideshow this afternoon."

Jimmy sniffed and pushed away from Peter. But he did not let go of Peter's hand. "Peter," he said in a shaky voice, "I was scared. Let's go home now."

Peter smiled, remembering what his mother had said. "All right," he answered. "Don't worry. I'll take care of you."

Suddenly Peter remembered something else his mother had once said to him.

"Sometimes," she had said, "children and even grown-ups show off when they're unhappy." Maybe that was why Jimmy had been showing off so much lately. Maybe he had felt lonesome and unhappy, too, since Mother had been away.

Peter took one last look at the shadowy open door of the next boxcar. He knew that the men would soon unload the big wagons. But Jimmy's little hand was warm and tight in his as they started back across the cornfield.

His Brother's Keeper

Peter was angry with Jimmy because he tagged along. But when Jimmy was in trouble, Peter ran to help him. What was Peter's main reason for helping his little brother? Write 1 or 2.

1. He was afraid his grandmother would blame him if anything happened to Jimmy.
2. He really cared for Jimmy and didn't want him to get hurt.

Peter wanted to see all the animals unloaded, but Jimmy asked to be taken home at once. Why did Peter do what his brother asked rather than what he wanted to do himself? Write 1 or 2.

1. He was afraid of the giant.
2. He wanted to take good care of his brother more than he wanted to see the animals.

Different Uses — Different Endings

Decide what forms of the underlined words should appear in the blanks. Write those forms on your paper.

1. As Jimmy tagged along, Peter said, "Why don't you stop __ after me? You try to __ along everywhere I go."
2. "Whenever you get into trouble, Jimmy, I get the blame," snapped Peter, frowning. "Why do people keep __ me for all your tricks? You should be __ for them yourself."
3. As the lights on the circus sign started to blink, Jimmy peered up at them and exclaimed, "Those yellow lights are __ terribly fast. They have __ ten times in five seconds."

4. Jimmy felt a <u>shiver</u> run up his back as the giant grabbed him. He ___ with fear as the giant picked him up, and he kept ___ until the giant put him down again.

5. Peter's little brother <u>sobbed</u> even after the giant put him down. "Stop ___," said Peter. "You're safe now, Jimmy. I don't like to hear you ___."

Words That Stand for Sounds

Look at what is happening in each of these four pictures. What sound would you expect to hear in each case? On your paper write the following sound words: *splash*, *rustle*, *crash*, and *chuff-chuff*. After each word, write the number of the picture that matches the sound.

Letters That Stand for Sounds

From the following list, write four words in which you hear long vowel sounds.

fade	lanterns	giant
object	Peter	pins
choke	worse	candle

THE SEVEN STICKS

A man had seven sons who were always quarreling. Whenever two of them started to quarrel, the others would stop whatever they were doing and start to quarrel, too.

Now because the old father was very rich, some bad men were looking forward to the day he would die.

They knew he would leave his land and his money to his sons. And they were sure that they could make the brothers quarrel among themselves about the land and the money. Then it would be easy to cheat the quarreling brothers of everything they had.

One day the father called his sons to him and laid before them seven sticks tied together in a bundle. He said, "I will give a prize to the one who is able to break this bundle."

Each son tried with all his might to break the bundle. After they had tried a long time, they all said that it could not be done.

"And yet, my boys," the father told them, "nothing is easier to do." He then untied the bundle and broke the sticks, one by one, without any trouble at all.

"Oh, well," cried the sons, "it is easy enough to break one at a time! Anybody could do it that way."

"You are right," replied their father. "And just as it is with these sticks, so it is with you, my sons. If you are divided among yourselves, it may come to pass with you as it did with these sticks.

"But so long as you stand together and help each other, no one can hurt any one of you."

United, we stand.
Divided, we fall.

An Idea That Lasted

Which of these ideas was the father trying to teach his sons in *The Seven Sticks?* Write 1 or 2.

1. If seven sticks are tied together, the bundle is strong.
2. If seven brothers stick together, the family is strong.

One, Two, Three, or More

Since there is only one vowel sound in the word *far*, it has only one syllable. Since there are three vowel sounds in *divided*, it has three syllables. The number of syllables in a word is usually the same as the number of vowel sounds.

Sometimes (as in the word *seven*), the vowel sound before *l*, *n*, or *r* disappears when you say a word fast. But you can tell that *seven* has two syllables, or parts, even if you cannot hear the second *e*.

Write the following words on your paper. Beside each word write the number of syllables it has.

Gettysburg	die	president	Meade
daughter	nickel	hospital	postal
consonant	cheat	retreated	licorice

In *doctor*, two consonants, *c* and *t*, stand between the vowels. The syllables are *doc* and *tor*. When two consonants stand between two vowels, the syllables are usually divided between the two consonants.

On your paper divide these words into syllables by drawing a line between the two consonants that stand between two vowels.

lantern	mistake	sorrow	enjoy	forget
quarrel	pinning	attack	person	unless

The Magic Button

The rowboat was drifting down the river so slowly that it seemed to be hardly moving. Mary Ann kicked aside a large pile of mussels to make room for her feet. Then she settled back to watch the well-known landmarks along the riverbank.

Her father steered the rowboat past the tall tree that meant they were getting close to home. It grew so near the riverbank that its bare roots could be plainly seen, like great black fingers holding onto the earth.

September had always been the month Mary Ann liked best. The days were just right, not too hot and not too cold. But now September meant something else, and the thought kept coming back to Mary Ann's mind to make her unhappy.

There was a big new school at Georgetown. And starting on Monday, Mary Ann must go to this big school instead of the little one-room school where she had always gone.

The thought of facing a roomful of strangers on Monday filled Mary Ann with dread. The children at the old school had lived on houseboats along the river, as she did, and she had known them for years.

The rowboat was nearing the houseboat where they lived. "I think I hear somebody playing a harmonica," her father said.

"It *is* a harmonica!" Mary Ann exclaimed, forgetting her dread for a moment. "It must be Uncle Andy!"

Uncle Andy was a sailor. Once a year he would come to visit them, with his songs and his music and his exciting tales of travel and adventure.

He was standing on the porch of the houseboat, with his harmonica in his hand, when their rowboat pulled up. He acted as if he didn't know Mary Ann in her blue jeans.

"Well, Tom," Uncle Andy said to Mary Ann's father, "I see you've got yourself a new helper. Who's this fine young fellow, anyway?"

"She's just about as good a fisherman as there is on the river," her father replied with a smile.

A tin-bottomed wooden tub, filled with water, was already heating over an open fire on the river bank. They had had an unusually good day, and the boat was full of mussels.

Uncle Andy helped them unload the boat and then clean the mussels in the shade of the trees.

The mussels were thrown into the tub of hot water to make them open easily. Then the shells were cleaned and put into piles. On Monday, the shell boat would come to pick up the mussel shells and take them away to be made into buttons.

"Look, I found a pearl!" Uncle Andy called out, smiling at Mary Ann. She ran to the tub to see what he was holding.

"That's not a pearl," she said. "That's nothing but a piece of shell. A pearl is round and smooth and full of pretty colors."

"You call that just a piece of shell? Why, that's as fine a pearl as ever I saw!" he answered, holding it up between his fingers. "That is, except for that black pearl I found off the coast of South America."

Uncle Andy's way of telling tales with a straight face made Mary Ann half believe them, even when she knew they couldn't be true.

She listened, now, as she worked, picturing in her mind the terrible deep-sea creature guarding the rocks where the pearl had been found.

When they finished working, Mary Ann took a bath. Then, feeling cool and refreshed, she sat down on the bank and looked out on the river. The sky was gray, with the first evening star appearing above the trees.

"I wish it could be like this always and always," Mary Ann said as her uncle came and sat down beside her.

"It seems to me that it always is," he said. "It was like this last year when I came, and the year before, too. The houseboats were tied to trees then, too, with the mussels in piles and the river running by."

"If I just didn't have to go to a new school!" Mary Ann burst out.

Uncle Andy looked at her, surprised.

"It was different at the old school," Mary Ann went on. "I knew everybody there. But I won't have any friends at the new school in Georgetown."

Mary Ann sighed. Uncle Andy did not know what it was to be shy with strangers. He would not understand her fear of stumbling over words in a reading lesson just because they had to be read out loud.

She half expected him to laugh at her, but instead he answered slowly, "Yes, I know how it is."

Mary Ann looked up quickly, but there was no smile on his face this time.

"There wasn't a shyer boy in the whole school than I was," he went on. "And it was even *worse* when I first went to sea.

"Why, I'd always be off in a corner by myself, playing my harmonica, while all the other fellows were having fun. Then one day I got the magic lynx eye. Everything changed after that. I could make new friends as easy as you please!"

"The lynx eye? What's that?" Mary Ann wanted to know.

"It's something I got at a strange port with a name I don't remember."

All of Uncle Andy's best stories began that way. And Mary Ann soon found herself listening, as she always did, half believing, even though she knew it could not be true.

She tried to picture her uncle, lonely and shy, as all the other sailors were leaving him to go ashore in some strange port. She could just see the old man who rowed out to the ship to trade a magic lynx eye for whatever he could get.

"Where is it?" asked Mary Ann when the tale was finished.

He shook his head. "I'm not sure I'll let you see it. I can see right now you don't believe me. Why, you might even call it a plain old button, for it does look like one. And could you imagine any lynx eye working magic after *that?*"

Mary Ann begged, and at last he went to the houseboat and came back carrying something in his hand. Mary Ann laughed when she saw what it was. It was nothing but a plain old button!

"I thought you'd laugh," said Uncle Andy frowning. "Of course, the holes make it look like a button. But they are to put the string through so you can wear it, like this."

He took a string from his pocket and put it through one of the holes. Then he tied it around Mary Ann's neck.

"I'm sure the magic would work if you'd wear it to your new school on Monday," he said. "All you have to do is look straight at the first person you meet and smile like this."

He smiled at Mary Ann in such a warm, friendly way that she could almost believe that what he said was true. "And you say 'hello,' like this. Then watch them crowd around you!

"Why, you should have seen how it was when the fellows came back to the boat after I'd got the lynx eye. It was 'Hello, there, Andy!' wherever I turned. You'd think I was their best friend!"

"Supper is ready," called Mary Ann's mother. "And any tall tale you're telling now will have to wait, Andy."

But he said not another word about the magic lynx eye until Mary Ann was leaving for school on Monday morning.

"Now don't forget to wear the magic eye," he whispered. "And mind you, you've got to believe in it and do what I said, or it won't work for you. You have to smile, like this."

His smile followed Mary Ann down to where she waited for the school bus. When she got on, the first person she saw was Susan, who lived on the hill above the river.

At first, Mary Ann felt shy and started to turn away. Then she felt the lynx eye, cool and round against her neck. She turned back to Susan, smiling, and said "hello" the way Uncle Andy had shown her.

Susan looked surprised, but she smiled right back and made room on the seat beside her. "You live on a houseboat, don't you?" she said. "That must be lots of fun."

"It is," Mary Ann said. Soon she found herself talking about fishing and swimming and rowing on the river as easily as if they were old friends.

When they walked into the classroom together a little while later, the others in the class turned to look at them. So Mary Ann smiled again, and wonder of wonders, they smiled back at her!

Could it really be that this button around her neck was a magic lynx eye after all?

When she rushed onto the houseboat late that afternoon, she called out to her mother, "Where's Uncle Andy? I've something to tell him."

Her mother looked up from her sewing. "Well, dear, I have something to tell him, too," she answered.

It was her mother who spoke first when Uncle Andy came out on the porch with his harmonica in his hand.

"I've sewn on all your other buttons, Andy," she said. "But there's one missing from your coat. I've looked high and low for it in that seaman's bag of yours, but I can't find it anywhere."

She held up the coat, and Mary Ann caught her breath. The buttons on it were just like the lynx eye her uncle had given her, and one of them was missing!

Uncle Andy looked at her and winked. Mary Ann winked back. "Here it is," she said, taking it off the string and handing it to her mother with a happy smile.

Magic or no magic, she didn't need it any more. She knew the friends she had made that day would still be her friends tomorrow, and all the tomorrows to come.

How the Magic Worked

The Magic Button shows you two kinds of magic. It tells about the make-believe magic of Uncle Andy's lynx eye and the real magic of a warm, friendly smile and a hearty hello. Answer these questions:

1. How did the make-believe magic help Mary Ann make friends?
2. How did the real magic help Mary Ann make friends?
3. Which kind of magic helped her more?

The Magic of Speaking First

Mary Ann found a way to overcome her shyness. As soon as she had smiled and said hello, she had no trouble in talking to her new friend Susan. However, some people still feel shy even after they have smiled and said hello. Those people cannot think of anything more to say to a stranger.

One good way to start talking with someone is to ask him a question.

1. Write the question that Susan asked Mary Ann when they started talking.
2. Write a question you could ask if you wanted to help a shy new classmate start talking.

When Did It Happen?

The following sentences tell five things which happened in the story. These sentences are not listed in the right order. Number from 1 to 5 on your paper. After the numbers put the letters in the right order.

a. Mary Ann and Susan walk into the classroom arm in arm.

b. Uncle Andy ties the magic lynx eye around Mary Ann's neck.

c. Mary Ann's mother shows Uncle Andy the coat with the button missing.

d. Mary Ann tells her uncle that she is unhappy about going to her new school in September.

e. Mary Ann smiles at Susan on the school bus.

From Letters to Lists

Look at the first letter of each of the following words, and list the words in alphabetical order.

dread	jeans
guard	television
lynx	harmonica
sewing	mussel

Look at the first and second letters of each of the following words, and list the words in alphabetical order.

winked	tub
stumble	worse
pearl	sailor
tales	port

Look at the first, second, and third letters of each of the following words, and list the words in alphabetical order.

bulldog	bare
blame	bet
button	burst
bench	boast

ALL THINGS BRIGHT

All things bright and beautiful,
All creatures great and small,
All things wise and wonderful,
The Lord God made them all.

Each little flower that opens,
Each little bird that sings,
He made their glowing colors,
He made their tiny wings.

The purple-headed mountain,
The river running by,
The sunset and the morning
That brightens up the sky.

AND BEAUTIFUL

The cold wind in the winter,
The pleasant summer sun,
The ripe fruits in the garden,
He made them every one.

The tall trees in the greenwood,
The meadows where we play,
The rushes by the water,
We gather every day.

He gave us eyes to see them,
And lips that we might tell
How great is God Almighty
Who has made all things well.

LOOKING BACK AND REMEMBERING
The Lessons They Learned

Write the name of the story in which a boy or a girl learned each of these lessons:

1. You like to be able to help your brother when he needs you.
2. Smiling and saying hello will help you to make friends.
3. There is just as much reason to be proud of a smart, friendly dog as of a handsome show dog.
4. Unkind criticism will cause hurt feelings.
5. Members of a family should stick together.
6. A little money can go a long way.

Write the name of the story each saying reminds you of:

1. United we stand, divided we fall.
2. You can't judge a book by its cover.
3. Smile and the world smiles with you.
4. You can catch more flies with sugar than with vinegar.
5. Waste not, want not.
6. I am my brother's keeper.

Sticking Together

Write the names of the stories in which these people helped each other:

1. Mary Ann and Uncle Andy
2. A father and his seven sons
3. Ben, Betsy, and Will
4. Dick and his mother
5. Peter and his little brother Jimmy
6. Billy, the doctor, and Pep

Between the Consonants

Write the following words on your paper. Divide them into syllables.

1.	excuse	6.	army	11.	soldier
2.	Lincoln	7.	capture	12.	object
3.	mussels	8.	September	13.	hugging
4.	warlike	9.	dreadful	14.	center
5.	fearful	10.	grabbing	15.	porter

The Sound Tells the Story

Say the names of the following pictures to yourself. In each row there is one picture that does not belong with the others. In the name of this picture you will *not* hear the sound which the letters at the beginning of the row stand for. On your paper write the names of the four pictures that do not belong.

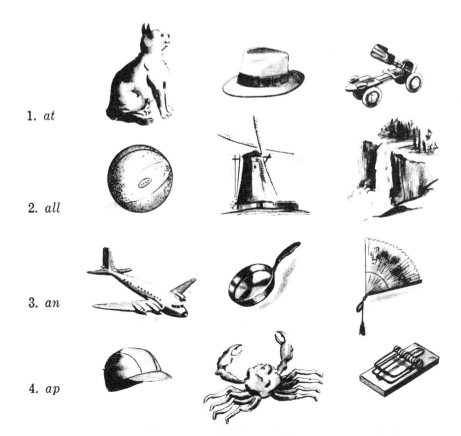

1. *at*

2. *all*

3. *an*

4. *ap*

Some Friendly Rhymes for Boys and Girls

There's magic in a smile, you know,
Because it always doubles.
You smile at me, I smile at you,
And we forget our troubles.

Don't say it if the word is cross.
Don't say it if you're mad.
Remember words can stop the game,
And then you'll all be sad.

Speak before you're spoken to —
A friendly word or two
Will help the other fellow
Who may be scared of *you!*

When you're feeling troubled
By something on your mind,
If you'll talk your worries over,
It will help a lot, you'll find.

No matter if you're quicker
Or slower than the rest,
The main thing when you're playing
Is to do your very best.

103

To give the other boys a turn
Seems dull or worse than that,
But just suppose *you* were left out
And had no chance to bat.

You'll find you'll make and keep good friends
If you will always do
To other people as you wish
To have them do to you.

By following this simple rule,
You'll see that this is true:
When you make others happy,
It makes you happy, too!

Winners All

Saying the Syllables

You have already learned that if you do not know the syllables of a word, you cannot say it. In your wordbook the first spelling, or entry word, has dots between the *written* syllables to show where they begin and end. The respelling shows how we divide the word into syllables when we *say* it. A hyphen (-) is used to show the *spoken* syllables, like this: \'präb-ləm\ \'krit-ə-siz-m\.

Why doesn't the word *lynx* have a hyphen in its respelling: \'lingks\?

Every respelling in the wordbook tells something else important. Say these two words, and listen carefully as you say them:

cush·ion   re·treat

In each word, one syllable is said more strongly than the other. Which syllable is it in *cushion?* Which in *retreat?*

Now look at the respellings of those words:

\'ku̇sh-n\   \rē-'trēt\

What do you think tells you which syllable to say more strongly? One little sign (') does the job. Where is it placed?

Now you have all the "keys" your wordbook can give you. Use them often as you read this unit.

The Miracle Miler

A soft wind blew through the open window of the bedroom, rustling the window shade. In his narrow bed over in the far corner, Glenn Cunningham lay with his face to the wall, sobbing with dread.

His mother and father and the family doctor stood close by. When his mother touched his shoulder, Glenn turned to face them, trying to hide his fear.

"You mustn't let them do it," Glenn begged, choking back his tears. "My legs will get well again, Mother. I just know that they will. Please tell the doctor they can't take off my legs. I can't run if they do."

"It'll be all right, Glenn," his mother said, trying to hide her sorrow. "The doctor has decided that he won't have to take your legs off. But you must have courage, son. You'll never be able to run again."

A flash of hope lighted the boy's tearful eyes at the news that he would be able to keep his scarred and lifeless legs. "Oh, I *will* run again, Mother!" Glenn burst out. "If you and Dad help me, I know I can do it!"

"Of course we'll help you," his father answered, swallowing hard to steady his shaky voice. "Your mother and I will do all that we can for you. But you can't expect miracles to happen, and the doctor says there's no hope for your legs."

"Never mind, son, what the doctor thinks," his mother said, blinking back her tears. "Maybe you *can* do it. Let's see if we can prove to Dad and the doctor that they're *both* wrong. Perhaps miracles *do* happen, if you just help them along."

Glenn grabbed his mother's hand and held it tightly against his hot face.

In the days and weeks that followed, those loving hands of his mother's were always busy helping Glenn.

She rubbed his legs until her hands were red. His father rubbed them, too. And at night, after his parents had gone to bed, Glenn rubbed them.

When he rubbed them, he could not even feel the touch of his own hands on his skin. It was almost as if the doctor had cut off his legs. They had no feeling in them.

"If only they would *hurt* me!" Glenn thought. "Feeling pain would be so much better than feeling nothing at all."

The nights were hardest, for at night, Glenn dreamed. In his dreams, he lived again through the fire in the little country schoolhouse, that had scarred his legs and killed his brother Floyd.

He would find himself fighting his way through the thick black smoke, shouting for his brother. Many times he would awaken crying, "Floyd! Floyd!"

The days, too, were long and tiresome. Day after day, with his father's strong arms about him, Glenn put his feet to the floor. Each time, he hoped his scarred legs would be strong enough now to hold him.

And each time, when they were not, he would cry, "I *will* walk some day! You wait and see!"

One day Glenn sat up as usual. He let his feet hang down, over the side of the bed. Suddenly he drew in a quick breath. His legs hurt!

"Mother! Dad!" he shouted excitedly, "Come quick! My legs are hurting me! I can feel them! They *hurt!*"

His parents came rushing into the room. Glenn lowered his trembling feet to the floor. His father steadied him until he was standing, and then he took his arms away.

This time, when his father's arms were gone, Glenn was able to stand alone. Not for long — only for a minute — but he *did* stand alone. Glenn and his parents cried for joy.

Little by little, during the weeks that followed, Glenn's shaky legs grew stronger. He could stand by himself a little bit longer each day, and he could even take a few stumbling steps. The pain was dreadful now. It seemed to get worse as his legs got better.

Glenn was always thinking of how much he wanted to run. "If I could just run," he said to himself, "the pain wouldn't matter. I'd be trying so hard to run, I wouldn't even notice." One day, to his great joy, he took a few running steps.

"It's true!" Glenn shouted, as he hugged his mother happily. "I don't notice the pain when I run!"

And so Glenn began to run. At first he could only run across a room. Then he ran to school. In a short time he was running everywhere.

One day Glenn ran to the market on an errand for his mother. In the store window, he saw a large silver cup.

"That cup will go to the winner of the mile race at the Elkhart fair next week," the storekeeper remarked, smiling at Glenn.

The rest of that day, Glenn thought and thought about that silver cup. How wonderful it would be if he could win it!

Glenn was proud of having learned to run again, and he wanted to prove to his parents that all their care had been worthwhile.

"I'm going to try it," he said to himself. "It can't be as hard to learn to run *faster* as it was to learn to run all over again. The last time I said 'I can do it,' I *did* it. Maybe I can do this, too."

It was a clear fall day for the Elkhart fair. Glenn liked the crowds and the dust, and the smell of the cattle. He liked the gay little stands with colored ribbons where the ladies were selling cakes and pies and candy.

Judges were walking about with paper and pencil, deciding who the prize winners would be. People were hurrying to the grandstand. It was almost time for the races to begin.

Glenn went with the rest of the runners to the starting place. They all ran up and down the track, warming up for the mile run.

"On your mark!" called the starter. "Get set! *GO!*"

The runners dashed down the track as fast as their legs would carry them, while the crowd cheered them on.

They passed the halfway mark. Suddenly Glenn moved ahead in a burst of speed. The boy just in front of him was slowing down. Glenn passed him, steadily picking up speed as he ran. He passed another boy, and then another.

Glenn could hear the loud breathing of the other runners as he passed them by. Now the finish line flashed into sight. It was coming closer, CLOSER, CLOSER.

Glenn threw back his head, lifted his arms, and shot across the finish line. The boy with the scarred legs, who had been told he would never run again, had won the race!

The judge handed Glenn the silver cup. His friends and parents came hurrying up to him. His mother's eyes were shining with tears, but this time they were tears of joy instead of tears of sorrow.

"It's a miracle, Glenn!" she cried, hugging him happily. "It's a miracle — a miracle."

Glenn had never been so happy in his life. How he wished his brother Floyd had been there to see him run!

Winning that mile race at the Elkhart fair made Glenn want to run in more races. He began to train himself, running for hours every day. His legs became stronger than they had ever been before the fire.

When he was in high school, he went to a track meet where he raced against boys from many other schools. There he won the world's championship for running a mile faster than any high-school boy had ever done before.

A few years later, when he was in college, he won a race called the Big Six Championship Race. This made him champion college runner of the whole United States.

Now Glenn decided to see if he could win the championship of the world. He entered races in many other countries. He did not always win. But every time he lost a race, he said, "I'll try harder next time. Next time, I'll win."

At last, the boy with the scarred legs ran the mile race faster than it had ever been run before. Glenn Cunningham became the champion miler of the world!

Brave Boy — College Champion

Glenn was badly burned trying to save his brother Floyd. The doctor was afraid he would never be able to use his scarred legs again. But Glenn did not give up. He kept trying until he won his fight against pain and was able to run well enough to enter races. The courage he showed when he was young helped him become a champion runner when he grew older.

Are you brave about bearing pain and sickness? Ask yourself these questions to find out whether you are in the same class with the miracle miler, Glenn Cunningham.

Number your paper from 1 to 8. Write Yes or No after each number.

1. Do you dash home from school at top speed whenever you have the tiniest ache or pain?
2. Do you cry when you get a little scratch?
3. Do you get angry if the doctor tells you to stay in bed a few days?
4. If you have to stay in bed, do you keep your mother running errands for you all day?
5. Will you swallow bad-tasting medicine without fighting or acting cross?
6. Will you stay in bed until you are well without coaxing your parents to let you get up?
7. Do you try to help yourself get well quickly by following the doctor's orders?
8. Do you try to act cheerful even if you have to stay in bed for a long time?

If you could truly answer No to the first four questions and Yes to the last four questions, you have a score of 100.

Listening for Vowel Sounds

Say the word *far* to yourself. Does the *a* in *far* stand for the *short a* sound, as in *hat?* No. Does the *a* in *far* stand for the *long a* sound, as in *ate?* No. The *a* in *far* stands for a different sound. You will find the word *far* in the Key to Sounds on page 282. The sound of *a* in *far* is shown by ä. This is the same sound as the short sound of *o* in *got.*

Look at the word *Elkhart* in your wordbook. The second spelling, or respelling, shows how to say the word. The first vowel has the *short e* sound, and the second vowel has the ä sound.

On your paper write the words below. After each word show its vowel sound.

barn   dashed   guard   blame   scar

The Vowel Sound We Use Most of All

Find the word *dumb* in your wordbook and look at its respelling. The vowel sound in *dumb* is shown by an upside-down *e* (ə), which is called the schwa. Now look at the respelling of *burst*. The vowel sound in *burst* is also shown by the schwa. The schwa is the sound that we hear the most often of all the vowel sounds. In the Key to Sounds you will see that the words *ago, up, perhaps, her, hurt,* and *bird* all have the schwa sound in them. Say these six words to yourself. Then say *dumb* and *burst.*

On your paper write the words below that have the schwa sound in them.

third   stumble   pearl   four   first
swallow   courage   nurse   won   fur

Too High a Price

"Ready! Get set! Go!"

Susan watched as the two bicycles raced away. "Hurry! Hurry!" she begged under her breath. "It's my turn next!"

Susan smoothed the wide blue ribbon tied to the handlebars of her bicycle and then pushed down on the back tire. Did it seem soft?

She peered after the two disappearing bicycles. They were out of sight now, around the curve.

Susan's thoughts raced with them along that first smooth stretch, down the long hill and up again. Hurry, Blue! Hurry!

Now she looked across at Virginia standing quietly by her bicycle with the bright red ribbon tied on the handlebars. She *had* to beat Virginia. She *had* to win this race for her team and for Miss Peterson.

Until Miss Peterson came to teach in the little country school, Susan had always sat on the sidelines on Field Day.

But Miss Peterson thought that everyone should have a chance to take an active part in the games and races. She said Field Day was for the whole school — not just for the boys and girls who could run fast or jump high.

"And that means me, too," Susan had thought happily at first. But what could she do?

She was never invited to be on a team or run in a race. She was fat, and she couldn't run fast. And balls always seemed to slip right through her fingers. So what could she do on Field Day?

Then Miss Peterson said they would have a bicycle race this year, and bicycling was something Susan *could* do.

Since then, at supper, she had said "No, thank you," each time ice cream or strawberry shortcake was passed. Susan explained to her parents that she wanted to lose weight for the bicycle race on Field Day.

The first time, her mother had looked at Susan in surprise. "My goodness!" she exclaimed, helping herself to some more shortcake. "No candy or cake *at all?* That seems too high a price to pay just to be in a bicycle race."

But her father shook his head, smiling at Susan. "No," he said. "You make up your mind if something is worth the price, and then you pay it."

The first few days, Susan had felt empty and cross. But she didn't give in, and now, she thought proudly, she was going to help win the race for the Blues.

"Here they come!" someone shouted.

With their red and blue ribbons streaming behind, the two bicycles raced into sight, side by side. The two girls pumped across the finish line at the same time. It was a tie!

Susan held tightly to her handlebars. The judge said, "The score is now one race for the Blues, one for the Reds, and two races tied.

"This last race between Virginia Williams and Susan Baker will decide which team wins."

Her mouth was dry and her knees trembled as Susan wheeled her bicycle into place beside Virginia's. It seemed to her that she'd never be able to get up on the seat and push down on the pedals.

"Ready! Get set! Go!"

Susan leaned forward, pumping hard to get off to a good start. Her feet were strong and sure on the pedals, and she began to pick up speed. Now she shot ahead of Virginia!

In her mind, Susan pictured Virginia as just a little figure, retreating farther and farther into the background, fading away as Susan raced ahead.

But when she reached the top of the hill and looked back, Virginia was close behind her, pumping steadily up the hill!

Susan was coasting down the hill now, flashing in and out of the tree shadows. "Win the race, win the race," her tires sang. She started pumping again.

Miss Peterson had said to take it easy the first half of the race. But how could she, with Virginia so close behind?

Susan slowed down to bump across a little wooden bridge. Her face was hot, and her legs were beginning to ache. As she pumped on, up a rise in the road, she thought longingly of the cool water in the brook.

She heard the bridge rattle as Virginia rode across.

Before she had even reached the halfway mark, Susan was breathing hard and her face felt hot and puffy. Her feet were slipping on the pedals. The hot road before her seemed to rise and fall as she blinked her eyes in the bright sunlight.

She could not keep from looking behind. Virginia was coming steadily nearer all the time, and she didn't even look hot.

Now the road curved around a small woods just beyond the farm where Susan lived.

Suddenly she thought of the short cut through the woods which she sometimes took on the way to school. She could save a lot of time by taking that short cut now.

Susan looked back again quickly. Virginia was out of sight around the curve, but Susan knew she was drawing closer.

"She's sure she's going to win for the Reds," Susan said to herself. "Well, she's not. The Blues are going to win." She turned sharply toward the short cut and was swallowed up in the welcome shadows of the overhanging trees.

She bumped steadily along. Carefully she steered her bicycle between the rustling branches of the low bushes that crowded both sides of the narrow, dusty path.

Once she almost fell when her front wheel hit an old tree root. How long the short cut seemed! She frowned, peering forward through the shadows. The path seemed to stretch on and on, endlessly.

At last she burst from the shaded path into the sunlight of the road again. Virginia was not in sight. She couldn't be ahead, she just couldn't! But maybe she was.

Susan forced her feet down hard against the pedals. Just one more little hill and then it would be a straight stretch to the finish line!

Her team saw her coming. "We won! The Blues are the champions!" they shouted.

When Susan coasted to a stop, they crowded around her, waving their blue ribbons in the air. "We won! We won!"

Soon Virginia rode across the finish line. "You certainly fooled me!" she called out to Susan. "I can't figure out how you could do it! I thought I could beat you, but after the halfway mark, I didn't even see your dust."

She jumped off her bicycle and reached out to pat Susan on the back. "That was a good race, Susan," she said.

Susan moved back quickly as the thought hit her like a sudden blow. "I *cheated!*" Did Virginia know? Did the others guess?

"I cheated in the race," Susan said to herself. "I took the short cut. But I wasn't thinking about cheating. I was thinking about winning.

"I did it for the Blues, and for Miss Peterson. But it doesn't matter whether I meant to cheat or not. It was still cheating."

She looked around at her teammates. She couldn't tell them now, not when they were so happy and proud of winning. She wouldn't be able to tell them later, either, or they'd never let her race again.

She was no longer hot, but cold and sick inside. And she couldn't lift her eyes to look at the chattering girls and at her teacher. Susan stood alone in the crowd, shivering with the ugly thought: "I cheated."

"Come along, Susan," she heard Miss Peterson say. The words broke through the wall that Susan was building to shut out the voices of her happy teammates. "The judge is going to read the scores for all the races. And your team won."

But Susan just stood there, digging her fingernails into her hands.

And then suddenly she knew that taking the short cut had been a mistake. It was too high a price to pay for winning. She swallowed the salty taste of tears.

"No," she said in a voice that sounded high and strange in her ears. "No. I — I got tired. I — I took a short cut. The Blues didn't really win."

There was a frightening silence. Then she heard Miss Peterson say in a warm voice, "Thank you for telling us, Susan. Better luck next time you race."

Only then did Susan look up. She was surprised to see that Miss Peterson did not look angry or disappointed. Instead she looked proud.

When Winning Is Losing

What is the bravest thing Susan did? Write 1, 2, or 3.

1. She tried hard to lose weight by giving up strawberry shortcake and ice cream.
2. She fooled Virginia by taking a short cut.
3. She told Miss Peterson that she had cheated.

If Susan had not forced herself to tell Miss Peterson she had cheated in the race, she would have been unfair to three people. How would her silence have been unfair to each of these people? Write your three answers.

1. Virginia Williams
2. Miss Peterson
3. Herself

The Reason

On your paper write the following words in two lists. In your first list write the words in which you hear a long vowel sound. In your second list write the words in which you hear a short vowel sound.

slid	rap	bet
waste	mix	choke
scrap	wrote	kite
sob	price	rise

Write the answers to these five questions:

1. What is the last letter of all the words in your first list?
2. Can you hear the sound of the last letter in any of them?
3. Is the vowel sound usually long or short in a one-syllable word that ends in silent *e*?

4. Do the words in your second list end with vowels or consonants?

5. Is the vowel sound usually long or short in a one-syllable word ending in one consonant, with only one vowel before it?

Map of Road for Bicycle Race

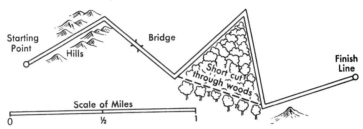

The scale of miles on this map will help you to figure out the answer to these questions. Write the four answers on your paper.

1. How many miles had Susan bicycled when she reached the finish line?

2. How many miles had Virginia bicycled when she reached the finish line?

3. How long was Susan's short cut through the woods?

4. How far did Virginia have to pedal around the woods?

Watch the Y's

Write the three words below in which *y* stands for the short sound of *i*.

bicycle   Anya   rhyme   salty   shy
actively   lynx   yelled   syllable   day

Built for Speed

Eddie Rickenbacker's father stood with his eyes fixed on his son in a stony stare.

Eddie faced his angry father fearfully. "But I didn't touch Mrs. Clancy's baby. I didn't even know the baby was there."

"You heard Mrs. Clancy calling!" Eddie's father roared. "Why didn't you stop? Why did you want Mrs. Clancy's baby carriage anyway?"

"I didn't want her baby carriage," answered Eddie, "or her baby either."

"You didn't want it!" Mr Rickenbacker shouted. "You saw Mrs. Clancy's carriage in her yard. You pushed it up the street as fast as you could run! And now you tell me you didn't want it! Then tell me, why did you take it?"

Eddie knew that he was going to have a very hard time making his father understand what he had just done. It was the quickest way to find out what he needed to know if he were going to win the race next week.

"Well, Father," he said, "I've been watching those new baby carriages. Their wheels seem to turn faster than the old kind."

"What do you care?" his father asked. "We're not going to get one."

"I know. But we're having a pushmobile race next week. I think I can win it if I have some wheels like the wheels on Mrs. Clancy's baby carriage."

"So! You thought —" Mr. Rickenbacker began. But Eddie stopped him.

"No! I didn't! I just wanted to find out what made Mrs. Clancy's carriage easier to push than ours. It was a trial run."

Eddie's father had always been glad that Eddie had an interest in learning how things worked. So now he asked, "Did you find out?"

"Yes," said Eddie quickly. "Those wheels have little balls of steel inside them that roll around when they turn, and it makes them run a lot faster."

"Balls of steel!" exclaimed Mr. Rickenbacker.

"Yes. They're called ball-bearing wheels. And I'm sure if my pushmobile had wheels like those on Mrs. Clancy's baby carriage, I could win the pushmobile race next week."

"Pushmobile races! That's all you boys think about!" said Mr. Rickenbacker. "Why don't you do some work for a change?"

"We do work. We worked hard to get the track ready," answered Eddie. "This will be the best race we've ever had."

Mr. Rickenbacker turned. "Well, don't let me hear of your using any baby carriage for another trial run," he said, and he walked up the path.

As soon as his father had gone, Eddie's thoughts jumped back to his beautiful, bright yellow soap box. Painted on it, in big green letters, was MILE–A–MINUTE–MURPHY.

Everything was ready now, that is, everything except the wheels.

"Somewhere, somehow, I just *have* to find some ball-bearing wheels," Eddie said.

Eddie could almost see MILE–A–MINUTE–MURPHY whizzing past the finish line. He was thinking so hard that he didn't notice the bumping of wagon wheels and the sound of a horse coming up the road.

It was old Sam, making his rounds with his scrap wagon.

"Any old clothes? Any old papers?" Sam called.

"No. None today," said Eddie. But then, at the sight of the loaded wagon, he whirled about and ran calling, "Wait, Sam! Wait!"

Sam drew his horse to a stop and waited.

"Sam, do you have any old wheels off a baby carriage?" Eddie asked breathlessly.

"Why, yes," answered Sam. "I think I have one or two pairs."

With one jump, Eddie was in the wagon. Yes, there were the wheels! He grabbed them up, one by one, and whirled them around in the air. Sam stared at him, wide-eyed.

Eddie's face fell, and he tossed the wheels down again. There wasn't one ball-bearing wheel among them.

"What's the matter?" Sam asked. "Don't those wheels turn all right?"

"Oh, yes, they turn all right," answered Eddie. "But I have to have the new kind, with ball bearings." Then he told Sam how he planned to use the carriage wheels to win the pushmobile race.

"I'll look, Eddie," offered Sam. "Maybe I can find some for you."

Eddie had little hope that Sam could help. Ball-bearing wheels were still too new. Not many people would be selling a new baby carriage.

Eddie was disappointed, but he felt certain that if he just kept on trying, somehow things would turn out right. "Never give up," he told himself.

He started for town. He walked up one street and down the other, looking in all the secondhand stores. But not one ball-bearing wheel could he find.

As the day of the big race drew nearer and nearer, Eddie began to get discouraged. He kept reminding himself that he shouldn't give up. That was certainly no way to become a winner.

Finally the day before the race arrived. Eddie went around to all the secondhand stores once more, but it was no use. Not one baby carriage with ball-bearing wheels had come in since he first started looking.

Late that afternoon, Eddie turned in at the gate of the Rickenbacker home. He was just going to be forced to put the same old wheels back on MILE–A–MINUTE–MURPHY.

Suddenly he heard Sam's voice calling, "Eddie! Eddie!"

Eddie whirled about and ran toward the gate. "Did you get them?" he shouted as Sam pulled at the horse's reins.

Sam's friendly smile was enough of a reply for Eddie. He was in the wagon with one big jump. There, at last, were two pairs of just the kind of ball-bearing wheels that Eddie had been looking for.

The crowd gathered early at the race track the next day.

All of the brightly painted pushmobiles were there, ready to go. The drivers climbed into their places and picked up their steering ropes. Then the pushers took their places behind.

Eddie knew he had picked the fastest runner on his block for his pusher. He turned and winked at him now. Only the two of them knew the secret of the four ball-bearing wheels. MILE–A–MINUTE–MURPHY was all ready to go.

The starter raised his arm. "Stay between your lines, boys!" he shouted. "And don't try to trip the pushers! Now ready, set, *GO!*"

The crowd roared, and the pushmobiles were off!

Drivers and pushers called to each other through clouds of dust.

Eddie held his steering rope tightly in his hands. Out of the corner of his eye, he saw that several pushmobiles had piled up on top of each other. But MILE–A–MINUTE–MURPHY whizzed on with its ball-bearing wheels fairly flying.

Just as Eddie had dreamed, MILE–A–MINUTE–MURPHY tore past the finish line with the other pushmobiles all trailing behind.

Eddie jumped out of his soap box and hugged his pusher. His friends came running up. They pounded Eddie and his pusher on their backs, shouting, "You've won! You've won!"

Eddie was grinning happily. Then he turned and pushed his way through the crowd to where his father was standing.

"It was those ball-bearing wheels that did it, Father," he said.

Mr. Rickenbacker laid his arm across Eddie's shoulder and chuckled.

"Don't you think you should give half of the prize to Mrs. Clancy? After all, it was her baby carriage you used for the trial run!"

Eddie Rickenbacker himself was "built for speed." When he grew up, he learned to fly. In World War I, he shot down more enemy planes than any other flier. The boy who wanted to be a winner became a man who helped his country to win a war.

Keeping Out of Trouble

At the beginning of *Built for Speed*, Eddie was in trouble with his father and Mrs. Clancy because he had taken her baby carriage. How might Eddie have kept out of that trouble? Write 1 or 2.

1. By running so fast that his father and Mrs. Clancy could not catch up with him
2. By asking Mrs. Clancy to let him use her baby carriage for a trial run when it was empty

Winning with Words

From the following lists, choose the word that should appear in each blank below. Write the six words.

whirl	steel	roared
tore	enemy	reins
built	pushmobile	whizzing
Sam	Murphy	racer

Each __ tried to take the lead,
But Eddie's car was __ for speed.
The minute he went __ by,
The people __ to see him fly.
He won the race in his __,
Which finished first on balls of __.

A Trial Run on Accenting

Say the word *candy* to yourself. You will notice that *candy* has two syllables, *can* and *dy*. You will also notice that the first syllable *can* is said more strongly than the second syllable. We say that the first syllable is accented.

If you were dividing *candy* into its syllables and marking the accented syllable, you would write *candy* like this: *'can·dy*. The mark (') that shows where the accent falls is called an accent mark.

Write the following words on your paper, dividing them into their syllables. Place an accent mark before the accented syllable in each word.

Clancy   swallow
carriage   unless
invite   Eddie

Step by Step with Eddie

The pictures above show six things that happened in *Built for Speed*. However, these six pictures are in the wrong order. On your paper write the numbers in the right order.

King of Baseball

The big man in the overcoat and cap tried to walk along quietly. But there was a stir as he passed. Heads turned to look after him, and the people in the hospital hallway stared and whispered excitedly to one another.

For the big man was the King of Baseball. He was the man who could hit more home runs than any other player.

He could not walk down the street without being followed by cheering crowds.

What was he doing here in the quiet halls of the hospital?

Babe Ruth stopped in front of a door and took off his cap. First he signaled to the man who was with him to wait for him here in the hall. Then he walked into the room where a young boy lay very sick.

The boy did not want to live any more. Pain hung like a thick, heavy curtain between him and all the world. He did not want to take the medicines his doctors ordered. He did not want to eat, or to talk, or even to open his eyes.

The stranger's voice broke through to him from beyond the heavy curtain of pain.

Slowly the sick boy forced his eyes open, just wide enough to see. Then he blinked, thinking the dream would fade away. But when he opened his eyes again, he was staring at the greatest baseball player in the world, sitting beside his bed.

Johnny Sylvester closed his eyes again quickly. Since he had been in the hospital, his mind had whirled through such terrible dreams that he always fought to wake up from them. Even being awake and feeling the pain was easier to bear than those terrible dreams.

But this one was different. For this was a dream that Babe Ruth, the King of Baseball, had come to visit a sick boy whom he didn't even know.

So Johnny closed his eyes again quickly, hoping he could hold onto this dream.

"Look, Johnny, look what I've brought you," the strange voice coaxed. And Babe Ruth laid a baseball bat on the bed beside Johnny's thin white hand.

Without opening his eyes, Johnny slid his thin finger tips along the smooth wood of the bat. The bat was hard — it was real! His eyes flew open and he smiled for the first time since he had been so sick.

The big man grinned back at him. "Johnny," he said, "do you know why I brought you the bat?"

Johnny could not move his head to shake it. He lay still, breathing quietly, and waited.

"I brought it because I want you to use it," Babe Ruth said. "And you can't use it if you keep on lying in this bed, can you?

"Now you listen to me, boy. Listen to your father and your mother, and obey your doctor. You take care of yourself, boy. Then you'll get well and use this bat."

A little color had come back into Johnny's white face. His eyes were shining as he watched Babe Ruth reach into one of the big pockets of his overcoat.

From the pocket he pulled a real baseball. Then he took out his pen, wrote BABE RUTH in big letters across the ball, and

The man who had come with Babe Ruth pushed the door open carefully and looked into the bare-walled room beyond. He saw that Ruth had given the boy the bat and the ball. He had made the sick boy happy.

Now it was time to go. Had Ruth forgotten he had to play a baseball game that day?

said, "This is for you, Johnny." Then he walked around to the opposite side of the bed and laid the ball on the bed beside Johnny's other hand.

Slowly Johnny curled his thin fingers around the ball.

Yes, the ball was real, the bat was real, Babe Ruth was real. It was not a dream! The most famous baseball player in the world had come to pay him, Johnny Sylvester, a visit!

The man tried to signal to Ruth. But the King of Baseball was taking off his overcoat and settling back in his chair beside the bed.

He started to talk about the different baseball teams and how each one played. He told Johnny some tales about famous baseball players. Then he told him how it felt to hit a ball and see it sail out beyond the grandstands.

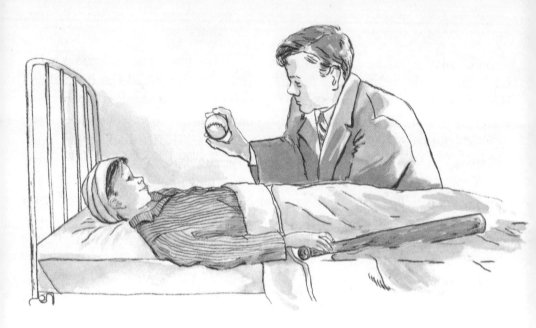

Encouraged by Babe Ruth's friendliness, little Johnny forgot how much it hurt him to talk. He started asking Ruth about famous games he had played in, and Ruth answered all of his questions.

Finally the big man stood up and started to put his overcoat back on. As he buttoned it up, he said encouragingly, "Now you must promise you'll get well soon, Johnny. And I promise I'll hit a home run for you this afternoon."

He winked at the wide-eyed boy and patted his hand gently. Then, with a smile and a wave of his hand, he was gone.

Babe Ruth kept his promise. He did hit a home run that afternoon for Johnny Sylvester.

And the boy lying alone in his hospital bed made up his mind to get well.

When the pain hammered wildly in his head, he would curl his thin fingers around the baseball and hold on. Johnny fought the pain by remembering that Babe Ruth, the baseball champion of the world, had come to the hospital just to see him.

Johnny began to get better. It took a long time. But at last he won his long fight in the hospital, and he grew up to be a strong, active man.

Johnny Sylvester was only one of the many children who had reason to love the great baseball player, Ruth.

People would come from all over the world to see him play. Presidents and generals were proud to shake his hand. But Babe Ruth, King of Baseball, never forgot the children who loved him.

He was never too busy to visit boys and girls who were sick in the hospital.

To these sick and unhappy children, Babe Ruth was able to bring new courage and new hope. And to some of them, such as Johnny Sylvester, he gave much more than a bat and a ball. He gave them the will to live.

The Present That Helped

Babe Ruth, the famous King of Baseball, was an unusually busy man. Nevertheless, he found time to visit Johnny Sylvester, a sick boy whom he didn't even know. Which of these things helped Johnny Sylvester more? Write 1 or 2.

1. Babe Ruth's bat and baseball
2. Babe Ruth's thoughtfulness and kindness

Quick Changes

The letters *re* can change the meaning of some words. When you write *re* in front of the word *made*, you have *remade*, which means *made again*. *Refilled* means *filled again*. A syllable such as *re*, added at the beginning of a word in order to change its meaning, is called a prefix. In the words *remade* and *refilled*, the prefix *re* means *again*.

From the following list, choose the four words that should appear in the four blanks below. Write those four words on your paper.

renew	restated	reprinted
rebuilt	retell	refreshed
repay	renamed	recalled

1. Johnny Sylvester felt happy whenever he __ Babe Ruth's visit.
2. At every hospital, children would beg Babe Ruth to __ the story of his first home run.
3. Whenever Babe Ruth visited sick children, he encouraged them to __ their struggles to get well.
4. When Babe Ruth stopped playing baseball, all the newspapers __ old pictures of him.

When You Visit a Friend Who Is Sick

When you go to see a sick friend, which of these things should you do? Write *a* or *b* for each number.

1. a. Play quiet games
   b. Play active games
2. a. Stay until your sick friend gets quite tired
   b. Leave before your friend gets tired
3. a. Tell your friend how much fun he is missing while he is sick
   b. Encourage your friend to try to get well quickly
4. a. Visit before or after dinnertime
   b. Visit at dinnertime

Two Words That Tell a Lot

If you were looking for *problem* on the wordbook pages in the back of your book, how would you go about finding the word? There is a quick way to find it. Look at the two guide words in heavy print at the top of each page. If *problem* would come between these two guide words in an alphabetical list, it would be on that page.

Decide which of the following words would be on a page for which the guide words were *opposite* and *struggle*. List those words in alphabetical order on your paper.

syllable	whom	salty
stir	vinegar	scraps
obey	Ruth	television
scale	sentence	pumped
prefix	classmate	Sylvester

The Good Sport

Jack Hill bounced his new basketball carelessly as he went walking along the street. He pretended he didn't notice the laughter and shouting of the boys who were playing basketball near Sandy Parker's house.

Then, out of the corner of his eye, he saw the boys stop playing. "Hey, Jack," one of them called. "Where'd you get the new ball, pal?"

Pal! These boys had never called him *that* before! What a difference just owning a new basketball could make!

"Oh, boy!" Brick Mayberry said eagerly. "That looks like real cowhide. Come on, Jack, toss me a pass."

"No. I haven't got time," Jack said, trying to hide how pleased he was that the boys had noticed him.

"Oh, come on, Jack!" Sandy coaxed. "Come on over and try a basket. Let's see if that ball is really as good as it looks. You can't tell just by bouncing it on the sidewalk."

Jack took his time crossing to the opposite side of the street. He pretended he didn't care whether they liked his ball or not. He walked up to the center of the free throw line, took careful aim, and flipped an overhand shot at the basket.

Even as the ball left his fingers, he knew that the shot was no good. The ball bounced off the basket. Sandy jumped into the air, grabbing it as it bounced away.

He snapped a quick pass to Brick. Brick took a few bounces, then whirled around, shooting the ball to Bob. Bob passed to Sandy, and Sandy popped it into the basket at the far end of the court.

"Hey!" Jack shouted, getting a little mad. "Hey! Give me back my ball!"

So Sandy bounced the ball back toward Jack. "Boy, Jack," he said as he handed the ball back, "that new basketball of yours is really a honey!"

"We wouldn't have much trouble in beating those Broad Street Bears with a ball like that, would we?" one of the boys said.

"Look, Jack," Sandy said eagerly, "what will you take to let us use that ball for our big game tomorrow?"

"Not a chance," Jack said. "Not a chance." This was just what he'd figured would happen. It made him feel good to hear these fellows praise his new ball and beg to use it.

Ever since they'd formed this team and started practicing, they'd been pushing him aside, saying he was too small to play on their team.

Now he smiled, looking at the old patched ball they were using. Tucking his own new ball under his arm, he turned and started across the street.

As Jack walked away, he heard them whispering behind him. When he reached the sidewalk, Sandy called out, "Hey, Jack, come on back a minute, will you?"

Now what were they going to try? Well, they wouldn't put anything over on him.

"Look, Jack," said Sandy, "we just decided to make you a member of the Brown Street Bulldogs."

"Fine," Jack said. "Wait until I take my ball home. I'll be right back."

"Oh, Jack," Sandy objected, "don't do that! Be a pal and let us play with it awhile."

"Come on, be a good sport, Jack," Bob coaxed. "We aren't going to eat your ball!"

"O.K.," Jack said slowly. "But you can't use it unless you promise to let me play. Just being a member of your team doesn't mean anything." It felt good to be able to tell these fellows what was what. "Do you promise?"

The Bulldog players looked at one another. Jack saw the uncertain nods of their heads. He knew they wouldn't dare to say no. That old ball of theirs wouldn't stand another patch. And what good is a basketball team without a basketball?

"All right," Sandy sighed, "you get to play."

"As much as I want?" Jack asked.

Frowning, the boys looked at one another again. "Yes, as much as you want," they agreed at last.

So the next day, when the Bears played the Bulldogs for the championship game, Jack was playing forward for the Bulldogs.

After about ten or twelve minutes of play, it wasn't hard to see which way the game was going. The Bears had captured the lead with a score of 9 to 4, and they showed no signs of slowing down.

Jack tried as hard as he could to shake away from the Bear guard. But their guard was much taller than Jack, and he was keeping Jack covered like a blanket.

Out on the sidelines, Bob, whose place Jack had taken, was aching to get in the game. There wasn't much chance of it, though. For just that morning, the Bulldogs' old ball had rolled into the street, and a truck had run over it.

Hearing that a member of the Bulldog team had a new ball, the Bears hadn't even bothered to bring their ball along. So now, without Jack's ball, the championship game would have to be called off.

No, there wasn't much hope for Bob. Jack had made up his mind to play every minute of the game.

"Let's go, Jack!" Sandy called, shooting an underhand pass to Jack. Jack reached for it, but the ball slid right through his fingers. He felt his ears turning red. No one else on the court would have missed a pass as easy as that!

But instead of criticizing him, Sandy just smiled at Jack encouragingly and said to him, "Don't worry. We all miss passes once in a while. You'll make up for it later on in the game."

By now, Bob was walking back and forth along the side-lines like a caged wildcat. But he didn't say a word.

At half time, the Bears had fought their way to a lead of 11 points. The score was 26 to 15.

The fellows didn't say very much as they sat resting on the bench. No one blamed him for the fact that they were losing, but Jack saw the looks on their faces.

As the team trotted out for the second half, Jack was sure he'd do better. But the harder he tried, the worse he played. He just couldn't succeed in breaking away from the Bear player who was guarding him.

Still there wasn't a word of criticism from his teammates.

Suddenly something dawned on Jack. His eyes were smarting. His breathing was painful. Every time he stopped running, his legs started to shake.

The truth hit him at last. He had made the mistake of trying to play basketball with a group of fellows who were far beyond his class!

They had been good sports about sticking to their promise, though it was certainly costing them the game. They had let him play just because he had the only basketball. Suddenly he felt like kicking himself.

"Time out!" Jack called. "Time out, Sandy!"

"What's the matter?" asked Sandy quickly. "You didn't get hurt on that last play, did you, Jack?"

"No," Jack said, "I want to go out. Bring Bob in."

For a moment Sandy stared at Jack questioningly. "You can play as long as you want to, you know."

"I know," Jack said. "But I've had enough for this time. Get Bob in here. He might make all the difference between winning and losing."

Then Sandy winked at Jack, and he nodded understandingly. "You're all right, Jack," he said. "We're proud to have a fellow like you on our team."

Jack watched the rest of the game from the sidelines.

With Bob back in his usual place, the Bulldog team speedily got control of the ball and tied up the score. During the last seconds of play, Sandy made a beautiful shot and the Bulldogs won the game.

Proud and happy, the boys formed a circle in the center of the court to give their team cheer. Suddenly Sandy shouted, "Hey, wait a minute! One of our teammates is missing!"

Turning to the sidelines, Sandy called, "Hurry up, Jack. You're in this, too, you know."

With a happy grin, Jack dashed out to join them.

Sandy was coming forward from the circle to meet him. "All you need is more practice," he exclaimed, throwing his arm around Jack's shoulder. "You may not be tall, Jack, but a fellow as *big* as you are belongs on our team, ball or no ball!"

A Sporting Boy and a Sporting Team

In the first part of this story, Jack did not act like a good sport. In which of these cases did he start to show good sportsmanship? Write 1, 2, or 3.

1. He pretended that he didn't care whether the Bulldogs liked his ball or not.
2. He agreed to let the Bulldogs use his ball only when they promised to let him play as long as he wanted.
3. He let Bob take his place on the team.

In which of these cases did the Bulldogs show good sportsmanship? Write 1, 2, or 3.

1. They used Jack's new basketball.
2. They did not criticize Jack when an easy pass slipped through his fingers.
3. They got control of the ball and succeeded in winning the game.

Listen for the Difference

The vowel sounds in three words on each line are the same. On your paper write the one word from each line in which the vowel sound is different.

1.	scale	aim	praise	bat
2.	cheat	creak	pep	peace
3.	price	light	guide	list
4.	force	shoot	score	court
5.	cub	pump	truth	dumb
6.	fade	Sam	pain	shake
7.	rise	limp	shy	die
8.	group	prove	whom	won
9.	fault	guard	broad	cause
10.	form	curve	bird	worst

Two for One

When you hear the word *bear*, you may think of a large animal called a bear, or of a boy bearing a pack on his back. In your wordbook you will often find more than one meaning for a word.

On your paper write the three underlined words below. After each word write the numbers of the two meanings that match it.

<u>aim</u>

<u>tore</u>

<u>trial</u>

1. Moved with great speed; dashed; hurried
2. The hearing of a case in court
3. The end for which one works
4. A tryout
5. Pulled apart
6. To point an object at something that one wishes to hit

LOOKING BACK AND REMEMBERING

Which Story?

Write the name of the story in which you read about each of these winners:

1. A runner whose legs were scarred in a fire
2. A basketball player who found out how to help his team
3. A racer who used ball-bearing wheels
4. A bicycle rider who said she had cheated
5. A baseball player who visited a very sick boy

Which Boy or Girl?

Write the name of the boy or girl who was helped by each of these people:

1. An old man named Sam
2. His parents and the doctor
3. Miss Peterson, the schoolteacher
4. Babe Ruth, the King of Baseball

Dictionary Tricks

Decide which of the words below should appear on a dictionary page for which the guide words were *court* and *famous*. List those words in alphabetical order. After each word, write 1 if the accent falls on the first syllable. Write 2 if the accent falls on the second syllable.

daughter	breathing	difference
discouraged	encouraged	excuse
Cunningham	criticize	delight
fooling	beyond	Elkhart
enjoy	curtain	figure

A Little That Tells a Lot

If you read this dictionary listing of *basketball* carefully, you will be able to answer all the questions about it. Write your answers on your paper.

bas·ket·ball \'bas-kət-bȯl\ **1.** An indoor game played with a big, round, air-filled, leather ball and raised baskets open at the top and the bottom. **2.** The ball used in this game.

BASKETBALL COURT

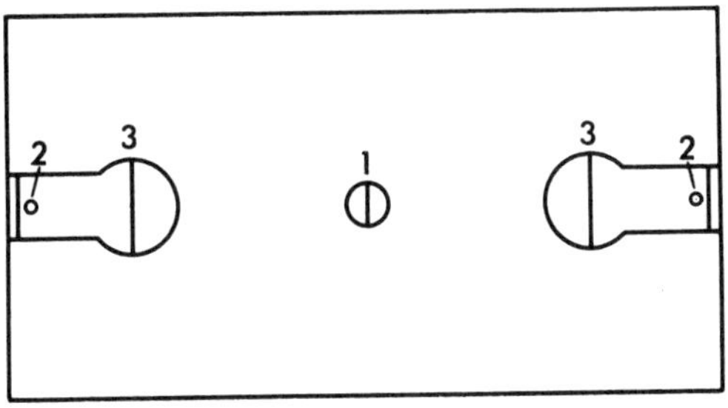

1 Center Circle
2 Baskets
3 Free-Throw Lines

1. What sound does the *e* in *basketball* stand for? The second *a*?
2. How many meanings does the dictionary list for *basketball?*
3. Would you find *basketball* on a page for which the guide words were *baby* and *barn?*
4. How many syllables are there in *basketball?*
5. On which syllable does the accent fall?
6. Are there any long vowel sounds in *basketball?*
7. In the picture of the basketball court, what do the 2's stand for?

A Rhyme to Read

B4 you go outside 2day,
C that you're nice and clean,
And when you play, don't T's your friends,
Or they will think U mean;
Pay close a-10-tion to your games,
But never shout, "I 1!"
B kind, and you'll make friends with E's,
And have a lot of fun.

Stories of Great People

Rules to Help You

Not all the new words in these stories are listed in the wordbook. So it is helpful to know some other ways by which you can learn to say new words.

Here are two vowel rules you have learned. An important word is missing from each rule, for you to fill in.

1. In a one-syllable word, ending in one consonant, with only one vowel before it, the vowel sound is usually ── (as in *hat* and *set*).

2. When a one-syllable word ends in silent *e*, the vowel sound is usually ── (as in *late* and *wide*).

Some consonant letters are as tricky as vowels are. Do you know why?

Say the words given below. Look carefully at the consonant letters as you say each word. Then decide which statement about consonants is true.

nice   cage   geese   easy

1. Consonants can be tricky because there are more of them.
2. Consonants can be tricky because they can have more than one sound.

What three consonants in the four words you said are the tricky ones?

In the rest of this book, you will learn more facts about the sounds in words. From these facts you can discover more rules to use as you read.

No Sacrifice Too Great

"Are you going to let me take a turn using your gun if you hit something?" Ted asked.

Walter Reed fingered his gun thoughtfully as they pushed through the underbrush. "No," he said, shaking his head. "No one is going to touch this gun except me — no one at all, not even you, Ted."

Ted stopped walking and stared disappointedly at Walter for a moment. "I thought we were friends!" he burst out at last. "Is that how you think friends are supposed to act?"

"That's not the point, Ted," Walter objected, hugging his gun with both arms. "You don't know how much trouble I've had keeping my gun safe from the Yankee soldiers."

Then Walter added, "I wish I had a nickel for every hour I've spent hiding it since the Yankee raids started!"

"Anyway, there's no use standing here wasting our time quarreling about it. You don't get to use my gun, and that's all there is to it. It's the only one left in our family now, and we'd have a hard time getting any food without it."

"Well, don't you think my family is hungry, too?" cried Ted, almost choking with anger. "The Yankees have taken every gun we had! I haven't held a rifle for so long, I can hardly remember what it feels like!"

Walter sighed. He knew he would never succeed in making Ted understand how he felt about his rifle. It was the first one he had ever had, and he loved it more than anything else he owned.

"Don't be mad at me, Ted," Walter said encouragingly. "If I have good luck hunting today, I'll give you part of whatever I shoot."

That seemed to make Ted feel better, and they walked along in silence for a while. Of course Ted's family was hungry. The way things were going these days, there probably wasn't a family in the whole South that wasn't hungry!

It was getting harder and harder to find any food since the Northern army had fought its way down into this part of Virginia. Everything seemed to be turning against the South in the war between the North and South these last months.

The boys were starting up a hill now. They were careful to keep well off the main road, in case any Yankee raiders were out hunting around here, too.

Walter was thinking about the chance that they might meet some enemy soldiers.

Suddenly he said, "You're not mad at me, are you, Ted? I didn't mean to make you mad before. But I just can't take the chance that you might be holding my rifle if we meet any Yankees."

"Well, what's the difference whether you hold the gun or I do?" Ted asked, breathing hard from the steep climb. "If we meet a Yankee, he'll probably grab the gun no matter which one of us is holding it."

"Oh, no he won't!" Walter exclaimed angrily. "That's *just* the difference. It's *my* rifle, and I'll shoot any man who tries to take it away from me!"

Ted looked more surprised than ever. "Well, that's the craziest thing I've ever heard of!" he cried. "You're the one who talks about wanting to be a doctor to fight diseases and save people's lives.

"Doctors don't go around shooting people! If you can even *think* such a thing, that shows you couldn't *really* care about being a doctor at all!"

"Oh, don't be silly, Ted!" Walter exclaimed. "Of course I do. I want to be a doctor more than anything else in the world. But when there's a war on, you have to think and act like a soldier."

"Seems to me," said Ted, "that when there's a war on, they need plenty of doctors, too. Otherwise, who will keep fixing up the soldiers so they can go on fighting?"

"So they can go on *raiding and stealing*, you mean!" said Walter, stopping to rest. "It's a wonder the Northern army has any soldiers left for fighting. The Yankees around here seem to spend all their time stealing our supplies!"

"What's that noise?" Ted whispered.

Walter's hands tightened on his rifle.

"Sounds like an old wagon on the hill," he said, after listening for a moment. "Let's go see!" Before Ted could object, Walter turned toward the main road, moving through the underbrush as quickly and as quietly as he could.

"Slow, now, boy!" he heard a man's voice calling. "Steady now, steady there, boy."

By the time the two boys reached a spot where they could see the road without being seen themselves, the wagon was drawing closer. Peering at it from the shadows, they saw it was carrying a heavy load of newly cut logs down the steep hill.

Now they made out the form of an old horse pulling the wagon, and the figure of a man in a faded blue uniform.

"A Yankee!" Ted whispered excitedly. "Look at his cap!" The wagon was opposite them now, in the center of the road.

"Yes," Walter agreed. "I guess he's taking those logs back to his camp. That's a pretty big load of logs for such an old wagon."

"Hey, look, Walter! That horse is really having a hard time keeping the wagon under control. The hill's too steep for him. He's . . ."

But before Ted could even finish his sentence, the tired old horse missed his footing and stumbled forward.

As the weight of the logs pushed forward, the horse was thrown to his knees. Then the wagon rocked back and forth for a moment, tipped over, and slid crazily down the hill.

When it came to rest at last, the sudden silence that followed the dreadful crashing noise seemed worse to Walter than the noise itself.

"Come on, Ted! Hurry!" shouted Walter, starting to run toward the road.

"*What?*" cried Ted, grabbing wildly for Walter's arm. "Are you crazy? That soldier is an *enemy*. You'll get yourself in trouble if you go near that wagon.

"If any other Yankees are around and they should see you, they might think *you* did something to upset the wagon."

Walter stopped, but only for a moment. Then he started forward again. "That soldier might be hurt!" he yelled.

He hardly noticed that Ted had whirled about and was running in the opposite direction, toward home.

Walter ran as fast as he could toward the overturned wagon. When he reached it, the horse had struggled to his feet and was pawing the ground excitedly. He was limping on one foot but otherwise seemed to be unhurt.

There was no sign of the Yankee soldier.

As Walter came up closer to the horse, a strange thought crossed his mind.

Why should he stay here and get into trouble? Why not steal the horse and hurry home? The Yankee raiders had taken two of his father's horses. So why not give them a taste of their own medicine? This was a chance to get even by taking one of the Yankee horses.

Just then, he heard a man's voice calling, "Help! Help!" It seemed close by, yet far away.

Guided by the direction of the sound, Walter dashed around to the other side of the wagon. He was stopped in his tracks by the most dreadful sight he had ever seen.

The weight of the logs sliding forward had torn the rope that was holding them to the wagon. The driver, unable to roll clear of the wagon as he fell, had been pinned under the sliding logs.

Walter dropped his gun and covered his eyes with his hands. It took all the courage he had to force his eyes open again and look at that soldier.

"Help," the man whispered. "Logs . . . move them . . ."

The pain must have been awful. The man seemed to be having trouble breathing, and his speech was hard to understand.

Suddenly Walter found himself talking. "It's all right," he said. "Don't worry. I'll help you. I'll get you out."

The fact that this man was an enemy soldier did not seem to matter any more. He was badly hurt, and unless Walter helped him, he might even die. Walter knew he *had* to help him.

The first log that Walter tried to move was too heavy for him, so he tried another.

As he struggled hopelessly with the second log, the man saw what was happening. "No use . . ." he whispered. "Weight too heavy for you . . . Fire your gun . . . My friends will hear . . ."

So, there *had* been a whole group of soldiers cutting logs. Of course, this man couldn't have cut them all by himself.

Walter reached for his rifle. But as he picked it up, fear clawed at his heart.

Would they take his gun, the Yankee soldiers, when they arrived? Yes, of course. They would surely take his gun!

For a long moment, Walter stood there, holding his beloved rifle. If only he could run home for help, and not have to call the Yankee soldiers.

But he knew there was no time to go for help. The man might die while he was gone. His friends were close enough to hear the shot of a gun.

Walter's eyes filled with tears, but to save a life, no sacrifice could be too great. Sobbing, he raised his beloved rifle for the last time and fired it into the air.

When Walter Reed grew up, he became a famous doctor and a leader in the fight against a disease that is called yellow fever. Thanks to his courage, and to the great work he did, man has finally been able to bring this dreaded disease under control.

In Washington, D.C., there is a United States Army Hospital which is named after him.

Walter Reed, M.D.

When Walter Reed ran to help the Yankee soldier, his friend thought he was crazy to let himself get into trouble. But Walter showed he had the heart of a doctor. Doctors often make sacrifices in order to help others.

What sacrifice would your doctor make for you in each of these three cases? On your paper write your three answers.

1. Suppose he was at a party, and you called him to say that you had broken your arm.
2. Suppose you asked him to treat you for a disease that he probably could catch.
3. Suppose you woke up in the middle of the night with a high fever and called him to say that you needed him.

Changes That Count

Each of the underlined words below is followed by three meanings. Change the underlined word three times to make three new words which will match the meanings. Write those new words on your paper.

bag

1. A tiny, crawling creature
2. Large
3. To ask strangers for money

pet

1. To place or to set
2. An object used for cooking
3. To tap gently

fill

1. Went down quickly
2. Able to hold no more
3. The time of year after summer

Small Changes

On your paper write the letter you must change in each of these words to make the name of the picture beside it:

main    steep

Two Vowel Letters with One Vowel Sound

Write the answers to the following questions about these words: *raid, speech, steal, supplies, jeans, aim.*

1. How many of the one-syllable words have two vowel letters but only one vowel sound?
2. How many of the one-syllable words have the long sound of the first vowel?
3. How many vowel letters do you see in the accented syllable of the two-syllable word?
4. Do you hear the long sound of the first or of the second vowel letter in the accented syllable of the two-syllable word?

One Busy Word

Write the word from the story that can name a President, an eastern city, or a western state.

You Can Teach Them

Deep in the woods of the Moses Carver farm there was a secret garden. It was a tiny garden, lined with neat rows of pretty colored stones. This garden belonged to a little boy, George Washington Carver.

George loved the spot in the woods which Mr. Carver had given him. It was his very own, and in it he could plant the flowers he liked best.

George's parents had died when he was a baby, and Moses Carver and his wife, who had no children, had taken George in. They loved the little Negro boy as much as if he were their own son.

George loved to work with flowers. He took care of all the plants and flowers in the big Carver garden and in his own little secret garden.

"You really have a way with growing flowers, George," the neighbors told him. "You would make a good plant doctor."

One day George finished his work and hurried to the woods to water the flowers in his secret garden. He walked along faster and faster until he could see the colored stones which marked the little spot of land that was his own.

George filled up a large tin can with water from the brook. But before he started to water the flowers, he pulled up a weed here and there and dug around the roots of the plants.

Stopping before the wild rose which he had brought here from a nearby field, he looked at the petals for a long time.

"I wonder why you have only five petals," he said to himself. "The roses in the big garden have more. Never mind. Someday I will learn all about you. Someday soon now, I'll be going to school."

George heard a step behind him, and looking around, he saw Mr. Carver. He jumped to his feet.

"Oh, Mr. Carver!" he cried. "There is so much I want to learn about plants and flowers. When can I start to school?"

"Why, George," Mr. Carver asked, "where would you go to school?"

"When I was in Neosho, I saw a school there," answered George.

"But Neosho is many miles away," Mr. Carver pointed out. "You couldn't walk back and forth every day."

"Maybe I could ride Rosie," George said hopefully.

"Rosie is the only horse we have," answered Mr. Carver. "I'm afraid I could not get along without her."

George touched the leaves of his wild bluebell. "I want to learn more about plants and flowers," he said. "I want to be a plant doctor."

Mr. Carver spoke lovingly. "Stay here and work in your garden, George. You can learn by doing."

"I can't learn much unless I know how to read," George said. "I want to go to school. I just *have* to."

After Mr. Carver had gone, the little Negro boy dropped to his knees. "Please, God, let me go to school," he begged. "Help me find a way so I can learn."

That night Mr. Carver told his wife what George had said about wanting to go to school.

"George is ambitious to learn," Mrs. Carver answered. "There must be some way we can help him."

One evening after George had finished the supper dishes, Mrs. Carver handed him an old, faded spelling book. "Here, George," she said. "I found this in one of my trunks."

George's face lighted with a smile. He reached for the book eagerly. "A book? For me? Can I learn to read from this book, Miss Sue?"

"Well, it will be a start, George," answered Mrs. Carver. "I will help you with it for a little while every day, after your work is finished."

That night, before George climbed into bed, he whispered, "Thank you, God. Thank you for the speller."

Early the next morning, he slipped quietly out of bed and put on his clothes. Then he tiptoed down the stairs, and out the door. He ran as fast as he could to the woodpile near the barn.

Never had he been so happy! He could hardly wait to finish his work so he could start his first reading lesson.

He filled the wood box in the kitchen. Then he hurried to the Carver garden. The birds were singing. The soft wind was stirring the flower petals and brushing across George's face. The ground felt cool and pleasant between his bare toes.

George stopped at a rose-bush loaded with beautiful red blossoms. "I'm going to learn to read!" he cried. "When I can read, I'll learn why you have so many petals and why my wild rose has only five."

When George had finished his work, he raced into the house, his brown eyes shining. "Good morning, Miss Sue," he called out. "I've done all my work. Will you help me with my speller now?"

Mrs. Carver laughed. "Yes, George," she said, "as soon as we finish the breakfast dishes."

From then on, the first light of morning always found George tiptoeing quietly out to do his work. Then he and Miss Sue would do a few more pages in the faded blue speller.

The winter passed, then the spring. George could now read all the words in the speller. But still he wasn't happy. He couldn't forget the school in Neosho. He spoke of it again and again to the Carvers.

One evening they talked it over again. Then Mr. Carver said, "George, you may go to Neosho, but we have no money to help you. You'll have to work to pay your own way."

So the next morning George started out. Under one arm he carried his faded blue speller and his neatly rolled-up Sunday shirt. In his other hand was his only pair of shoes.

It was a long, dusty road that he had to travel. But it was the road that led to learning, so his heart was as light as the songs of the birds in the trees.

Someday he'd come back, and then he would teach other people who wanted to learn as he did now. He'd be able to teach them all about plants and how to make them grow better.

Many years later, Professor George Washington Carver sat on a hill overlooking the college where he was a teacher.

The young plant doctor was remembering that long walk to Neosho when he was a little boy. It had taken a lot of courage for him, then, to leave his secret garden and all the friends he loved.

And after he had learned all he could at Neosho, it had taken courage to pull up his roots again. But once more, he had found the courage he needed.

He had left Neosho and had gone on, in search of still higher learning. He had worked night and day to earn his way through college. And then, at last, after years of struggle, he had become the plant doctor that he had always dreamed of being.

Professor Carver knew that he needed some of that courage now. He touched the letter on his knee and then turned to look at the grounds of Iowa State College. The grass was a deep, rich green, and the blossoms in the flower beds were bright with color.

He was proud to be teaching at such a fine college. He was proud of the grounds he had made beautiful, proud of the students whom he was teaching to be plant doctors, too.

"Show me the right way, God," he said now, picking up the letter. "Help me to give the right answer."

The letter was from Booker T. Washington. He was a Negro, like Professor Carver, and he wanted to help his people. So he had started a small college for Negroes, which was called Tuskegee Institute.

He was writing Professor Carver to ask him to give up his work at Iowa State College and come to teach at Tuskegee Institute. Professor Carver read the letter once more. "I cannot offer to make you a great man," the letter said.

"I don't care about being great," Professor Carver said to himself. "But I *am* proud of being a teacher here at Iowa State College. It's like home to me now — the teachers, the students, the grounds I have made beautiful."

The letter went on: "I cannot offer you money, because we have hardly enough to keep the college going. I can only offer you hard work. Of that, there will be plenty."

Professor Carver sat staring at the page thoughtfully. "I am not afraid of work," he said to himself. He let the letter fall to the ground. He did not need to read the next lines. He knew them already.

"I can only say that our people need you. They do not know how to work their farms. They need someone to show them a better way of life, how to be strong and useful. You are the one. You can teach them."

Those words were running through his mind over and over again. "You can teach them, you can teach them." Somehow, they seemed to have a special meaning for him. Then, from out of the past, he remembered.

It was his promise. When he started to Neosho, he had promised himself, "Someday I will come back and teach other people who want to learn about plants."

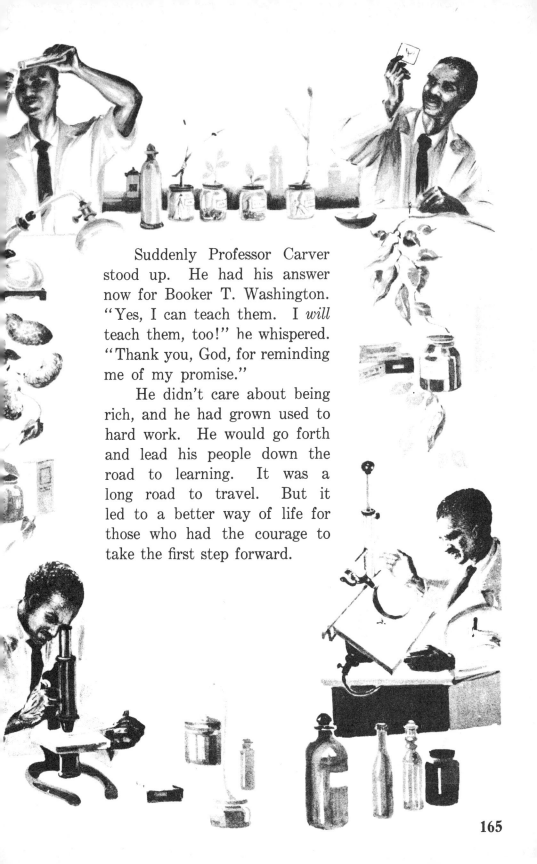

Suddenly Professor Carver stood up. He had his answer now for Booker T. Washington. "Yes, I can teach them. I *will* teach them, too!" he whispered. "Thank you, God, for reminding me of my promise."

He didn't care about being rich, and he had grown used to hard work. He would go forth and lead his people down the road to learning. It was a long road to travel. But it led to a better way of life for those who had the courage to take the first step forward.

Getting Ahead

George Washington Carver started as a poor farm boy, but he kept going to school and studying until he became a great professor. For this Negro boy, the ladder of learning was the ladder of success.

Each of the following three schools was a step on George's ladder of success. On your paper draw a ladder with three steps. Write the names of these schools in the right order on the steps, beginning at the bottom.

a. Iowa State College
b. School at Neosho
c. Tuskegee Institute

Help in Getting Ahead

From a poor farm boy with only one Sunday shirt, George Washington Carver rose to be a great man. He helped himself to get ahead, and he had help from others. As a boy and as a man, he never forgot to thank God for helping him.

Choose the words which will make each of the following sentences right. On your paper write the words you choose.

1. George learned to read from (a spelling book, a storybook).
2. (Moses Carver, Sue Carver) helped George to learn to read.
3. George Washington Carver wanted to be a plant doctor so that he could (become rich, help others).
4. He became a great plant doctor because (he loved to work with plants, he loved to teach college students).
5. He became a great college professor because (he loved to work with plants, he loved to teach college students).
6. When we say he was ambitious, we mean that (he worked hard to get what he wanted, he knew about petals and blossoms).
7. Booker T. Washington asked Professor Carver (to make the grounds beautiful, to teach) at Tuskegee Institute.
8. Professor Carver decided to go to Tuskegee Institute because (he wanted to be famous, he remembered his promise to go back and teach others).

The American Way

She looked out on the noisy street, crowded with carriages and horse-carts. In front of Hull House, a man was pulling a boy along the sidewalk. The boy was holding back as hard as he could, his heavy shoeshine box banging against his legs.

"Please don't take me to the police, Sam!" the boy was begging. "I wasn't the one who did it, really I wasn't!"

"I didn't do it, Sam! I tell you, I didn't push over your cart!"

The voice that drifted in through the open window was more than just excited. There was fear in it, too, and it was the fear in the voice she heard that pulled Jane Addams to her window.

"Tell that to police!" the man yelled in broken English. "Police man know how to fix bad boy like you!"

"I'm not bad! I didn't do it, Sam!" the boy cried. Just then, he caught sight of Miss Addams peering out of her open window. "Ask Miss Addams!" the boy shouted. "She knows me. She'll tell you I'm not bad! Miss Addams! Please help me, Miss Addams!"

In answer to his frightened appeal, Miss Addams waved at the man, calling, "Please wait a minute, sir! I'm coming out!"

A few moments later, she was standing on the sidewalk beside the angry man and the frightened boy.

The man stopped pulling at the boy and stared in surprise at the young woman.

She was speaking to him, but her words were not those strange English sounds which were so hard for Sam to understand. She spoke in his own language — the language of the country Sam had left just a few months before.

At the sound of his own beloved language, Sam forgot, for a moment, to be angry. But then he remembered his overturned cart and all his lovely fruit and vegetables that were rolling around in the street.

There was nothing left that he could sell. And even on days when he sold *all* of his vegetables and fruit, they never brought in enough money.

There wasn't enough money to buy all of the food that his six children needed. And there was never enough to pay for a better place for his crowded family to live in.

Now this boy, Tony, had pushed over the vegetable cart. Sam pulled at Tony. "Come, you bad boy," he said, with anger rising again in his voice. "I take you to police."

"No! No! I didn't do it, Miss Addams!" Tony cried. "I didn't do it, and that's the truth."

Miss Addams said gently, "Sam, did you *see* Tony do it? Did you see him with your own eyes?"

"No," Sam replied slowly. "I did not see Tony with my own eyes. But he did it."

"Let's go inside and talk this over, Sam," Miss Addams said. "I know Tony. He isn't bad. If you didn't really *see* him do it, you may be wrong in thinking he was the one who upset your cart. You should give Tony a chance to explain."

Unwillingly, Sam followed Miss Addams toward the open doorway of Hull House.

He had heard a lot about this Miss Addams and her Hull House. Many people in their neighborhood had told him about her. They said she spent all her time helping people who were sick or in trouble.

He knew she had clubs for boys and girls, and big rooms where they could play safely, away from the crowded streets.

Mothers who had to go to work could bring their little children to Hull House. They could leave them there to be cared for all day without paying any money.

Miss Addams must be a good lady, Sam thought, but she could not bring back his fruit and his vegetables.

Sam was following her now down a long hallway and into a big room beyond. He looked wonderingly at the soft chairs, the beautiful curtains at the windows, and the pictures on the walls. Then he sat down carefully opposite Miss Addams.

"Sam," she began quietly, "things are different, here in America, from the way they are in other countries. We do not call a person bad unless we can prove he has done something wrong. We don't decide who is at fault until we know all the facts.

"Now this problem between you and Tony is an important problem. So let us handle it the American way.

"First, you explain to me what happened, and then we'll let Tony tell about it his way."

Sam sighed hopelessly. He wasn't angry any more. He was beginning to think that it didn't really matter, anyway, who had overturned his cart.

All that mattered was that he would have no money. Now his children would feel, more than ever, the hollow pain of hunger.

Miss Addams listened while Sam told her how he had left his cart unguarded for a few minutes. As he hurried back, he heard boys shouting, and then a loud crash. But when he reached his overturned cart, only Tony was standing there.

Somehow, as Miss Addams kept looking at him steadily with her kind and friendly eyes, Sam wasn't so sure that Tony was to blame. "Other boys I saw, maybe, out of the corner of my eye. But this Tony, he didn't have time to run . . ." Sam's voice trailed away.

Then Tony told his story. He spoke quietly, and the fear was gone from his voice. Miss Addams had known him a long time. She knew he wouldn't lie to her. He felt he could trust her to make Sam understand that he was telling the truth.

"I had just finished shining a man's shoes," Tony said. "I heard a crash across the street, and I ran over to see what had happened. Four or five boys were running away.

"Then Sam rushed up and grabbed my arm. But honestly, Miss Addams, Sam is mistaken. I wasn't the one who tipped over his cart."

Miss Addams turned to Sam. "I believe that Tony is telling us the truth," she said. "And I would like to tell you why I trust him.

"Is it all right if he goes now, Sam, and we can sit and talk for a little while?"

Sam nodded.

Then Tony flashed a wide grin at Miss Addams and raced out of the room.

Miss Addams, watching him go, said quietly, "Tony is a good boy, Sam. He has been in our Boys' Club ever since we started it.

"It was hard for us at first," she went on. "The boys did not understand that we were trying to help them. Tony was one of those who helped me to teach the others."

"But that doesn't prove that Tony didn't push over my vegetable cart!" Sam objected.

"No, perhaps not, but let me finish," said Miss Addams. "I have never known Tony to lie or cheat or to do anything ugly or unkind. Even when he broke a window once, by mistake, he came right away to tell me.

"Pushing over your cart was an ugly thing to do. I am sure that Tony is telling the truth when he says he did not do it. Please believe me."

Sam thought it would be impossible not to believe this quiet, kind young woman with the honest gray eyes. "Yes," he said, "I believe you." But fear lay heavy in his heart. How would he feed his family next week?

He stood up and started to speak. Then he swallowed hard and stopped. He was too proud to ask for help.

But Miss Addams was looking at Sam. She saw the fear in his eyes and guessed the reason for it. "Sam," she said gently. "I know you have lost everything you could sell this week. You are worried that your family will be hungry.

"We keep some money here at Hull House to give to people in the neighborhood when they need it. Please let me give you enough to buy more fruit and vegetables for your cart."

Sam stared at her, speechless with surprise. "Money?" he asked at last. "Money to buy more vegetables?"

Miss Addams nodded and walked quickly to her desk in one corner of the room.

Sam watched her, his heart fairly bursting with joy. To talk things over, this American way, was good. And to help other people, that was good, too. American ways were good ways. A man could be happy with neighbors such as these.

"I will pay you back!" Sam cried. "Little by little, each week, Miss Addams, I will pay you back."

She brought him some bills and pressed them into his hand. "There," she said, "that should be enough."

"Oh, thank you!" Sam cried. "Thank you, Miss Addams, for me, and for my family, too. You are a good woman.

"I hear you take care of little children. And I hear you help the boys and girls — even the mothers and the fathers. But I did not know you understand about hunger."

He ducked his head, turning a little red. "A speech I make," he said, backing away toward the door. "A speech I make instead of a song. But my heart, it is singing, 'Thank you, thank you, Miss Addams.'"

Are You a Good Neighbor?

A good neighbor like Jane Addams tries to help everyone — her family, her friends, and even people who live outside her neighborhood. How good a neighbor are you? Find out by asking yourself these questions. Write Yes or No for each question.

1. Do you help your mother with the dishes?
2. Do you cheerfully run errands for both of your parents?
3. When your clothes have been freshly cleaned and pressed, do you try to keep them neat?
4. When someone in your class is sick, do you visit him?
5. If your friend Tony has no skates of his own, will you trust him with yours?
6. If you know how to ride a bicycle but your friend doesn't, will you teach him?
7. When someone new enters your class, do you help him find his way around the school?
8. Instead of throwing away your old clothes, do you send them to poor children across the sea?
9. If you see a stranger fall down on the playground, do you run quickly to help him?
10. When your club fills a Christmas basket for a needy family, do you try to bring as much food as you can?

If your first three answers are Yes, you are a good neighbor to your family. If you honestly answered Yes to questions four, five, and six, you are a good neighbor to your friends. If you answered Yes to the last four questions, you are like Jane Addams — a good neighbor even to strangers. What is your score?

Finding an Answer

If you have ever had a quiz show in your class, you may have found that one person cannot know all the answers. But one person can find most of the answers in a book or set of books called an encyclopedia. Names of people, places, and things are listed in an encyclopedia in alphabetical order.

Read what your school encyclopedia says under *Addams, Jane.* On your paper write the letter of the right ending for each of these sentences.

1. Jane Addams was born between:
    a. 1825 and 1850.
    b. 1850 and 1875.
    c. 1875 and 1900.
2. Jane Addams helped needy families because:
    a. her own family had always been poor.
    b. she never had enough money for college.
    c. she had seen the dirty, broken-down homes in which some families had to live.
3. Jane Addams started Hull House with:
    a. Ellen Gates Starr.
    b. Ellen Hull.
    c. Ellen Greenway.
4. Jane Addams wrote a book called:
    a. *Hunger at Hull House.*
    b. *Twenty Years at Hull House.*
    c. *The Impossible Piece of Work.*

BROTHER FRANCIS

More than seven hundred years ago, in a country that is far beyond the sea, a man was walking toward a town called Gubbio. As he went along the dusty road, his voice filled the air with singing.

Brother Francis would often sing as he walked from town to town, bringing help and comfort to those who needed him. He sang of the sun which warmed him, and of the rushing waters of the stream that cooled his tired feet.

Adapted from *God's Troubadour*, by Sophie Jewett

He sang of the birds and animals which he loved because God had made them, even as He had made man.

But on this day, as Brother Francis drew near to the little city of Gubbio, he stopped his singing.

Where were the men who should be faithfully watching their sheep on the blossom-covered hillsides? Where were the merry children who usually came running to meet him?

Brother Francis quickened his step and hurried toward the gates of the city. But when he reached them, he found they were closed.

He knocked, and the gates were quickly opened. But as soon as he had stepped inside, they were quickly closed again behind him.

With trembling voices, the people of Gubbio told Brother Francis of their terrible fear. A great wolf had appeared in their neighborhood. He would wander the countryside day and night, killing their sheep and their goats and attacking men, too, whenever he met them.

Children could no longer run and play on the flowered hillsides. Even the bravest of the men were afraid to go out to guard their sheep and reap the wheat in their fields. For the wolf was as strong as three hunters.

Brother Francis listened to their dreadful tales.

He understood their fear, but he himself was not afraid. For the same God who had made him, had made the wolf. And Francis believed in his heart that every creature God had made was his brother or his sister.

To the great surprise and fright of the people of Gubbio, Brother Francis said that he would himself go out and find the wolf.

The people begged him not to go, but Brother Francis told them to have no fear and went forth at once from the city.

Behind him came the bravest men of Gubbio. Though still frightened, they were a little quieted by the courage of this man whose great faith was like a shield before him.

Not far beyond the city gates, where a wood of tall oaks shadowed the road, the men saw the wolf and stopped. The beast was coming along with his great red mouth open, ready to spring upon Brother Francis.

But Brother Francis walked steadily on. He went, not as a soldier goes to do battle with an enemy, but as one might go out to meet a friend.

As the unarmed man and the wild beast neared each other, Francis called out cheerfully, "Come here, Brother Wolf! I appeal to you, in the name of God, to do no harm to me or to any of these men."

Then, with great wonder, the men saw that the terrible wolf stopped running, and that the awful mouth closed. And presently, the big creature came softly up to Brother Francis and, quiet as a lamb, lay down at his feet.

Francis began to speak to him gently, as one man might reason with another.

"Brother Wolf, you have been doing much harm throughout this countryside, hurting and killing God's creatures, both men and animals. I know that it is from your hunger, and only from your hunger, that you do these bad things.

"But the people do not understand this. In their fear, they cry out against you, and every man is your enemy."

The wolf lay still, resting his head on his paw.

"I wish," Brother Francis went on, "to make peace between you and the people of Gubbio. If you will promise to do no more harm to man or beast, I will promise you this.

"You will never be hungry again, and there will be no more reason for you to kill your fellow creatures. Will you promise me, then, Brother Wolf, that you will do no more harm from this time forth?"

The wolf, who seemed to have been listening carefully, nodded his great head.

Then Francis added, "Now Brother Wolf, I want you to make me so sure of your promise that I cannot doubt it."

The man held out his hand, and the beast lifted his big paw and laid it gently on the hand of Brother Francis. It was as if he wanted to say, "Here is my hand. I will keep my part of the promise."

"And now," said Francis, "come with me, Brother Wolf, and do not be afraid." Then he turned toward the city, and the wolf walked beside him like a pet lamb. The brave men of Gubbio followed in wonder.

Once within the city, all of the people, young and old, crowded about to see Brother Francis and the wolf. "It is a miracle," they whispered.

Francis stood in the market place with the wolf at his side. His voice rang out across the silence of the wondering crowd.

"Listen, my friends," said Francis. "Brother Wolf, who is here before you, has promised never to hurt you again. It is only because of hunger that he has done you harm.

"If you, in your turn, will promise never to let him go hungry again, he will have no reason to break his promise."

Then all of the people, as if with one voice, promised to feed Brother Wolf and do him no harm. They shouted for joy that God had sent unto them so good a man, to save them and bring peace to their city again.

From this day on, Brother Wolf lived in Gubbio. He went about from door to door, even entering the houses, without doing any harm. Neither was he harmed by anyone, but was well fed and kindly treated, and not a dog dared to bark at him.

The sight of the big wolf walking so peacefully through their streets came to be a happy sight to the eyes of the people.

It helped them to remember always the great goodness of Brother Francis, the man who loved every creature that God had made.

"He prayeth best who loveth best
All things both great and small;
For the dear God who loveth us,
He made and loveth all."

To Kill or to Love

When the people asked Brother Francis to shield them from the wolf, he could have brought comfort to them by killing the beast. Instead, he treated the wolf as if it were his brother.

Why didn't he kill the wolf? Write 1 or 2.

1. He doubted that he could win a battle with a wild beast.

2. He believed in giving love unto all God's creatures.

A Pair of Prefixes

When you say that a country is *undivided*, you mean that it is *not divided*. When you say that a class is *disorderly*, you mean that it is *the opposite of orderly*. The prefixes *un* and *dis* can mean *not* or *the opposite of*.

Un and *dis* appear as prefixes on six of the words given in the following sentences. Choose the word that will carry out the right meaning for each sentence. On your paper write the words you choose.

1. The (friendly, unfriendly) wolf was making the people of Gubbio (happy, unhappy).

2. Suddenly the wolf (appeared, disappeared), and Brother Francis spoke (kindly, unkindly) to the beast.

3. The wolf never (obeyed, disobeyed) Brother Francis and faithfully followed him everywhere.

4. After that, the men of Gubbio were (afraid, unafraid) to go out to their fields to reap their wheat.

MAP OF ITALY

North

West

East

KEY

Mountains
Lowlands
Water

Scale of Miles

0   50 100   200

South

Map of Italy

The town of Gubbio is in a country called Italy. This map shows the mountains and lowlands of Italy. The little black spot shows where Gubbio is.

If you read this map carefully, you will be able to answer the following questions. Write the answers on your paper.

1. What does the shape of Italy remind you of?
2. Is the town of Gubbio in the mountains or in the lowlands?
3. Are there mountains or lowlands in the most northern part of Italy?
4. Is Gubbio on the seacoast of Italy or toward the middle of the country?
5. Are there mountains or lowlands along the eastern coast of Italy?
6. Is Gubbio about 200 or about 400 miles from the southernmost tip of Italy?

A Harvest to Remember

With one last rattle, the new reaper stopped in a great cloud of dust. Tossing the reins to his younger brother, Cyrus McCormick said, "Here, take this thing to the barn, Bill. It's no good."

For a moment, William just stared at him, speechless with surprise. "No good!" he cried at last. "But I thought that it was a success! What do you mean, it's no good? It cut the wheat, didn't it?"

Cyrus turned to his father, his face sad and discouraged. "It's not right yet, Father," he sighed. "I'll have to work on it some more."

Mr. McCormick looked as surprised as William had been. "But it *did* cut the wheat all right, Cyrus," he said. "It's a good reaper."

"Sure it's a good reaper!" William piped up. "Every wheat farmer in the neighborhood will probably want one. In fact, I'll bet every farmer in the whole country will want one!"

Cyrus pointed to a line of fallen wheat behind the right wheel of the reaper. "Look," he said. "The machine knocks down too much wheat."

"It hasn't knocked down very much," said William. "And think of the time that farmers will save. It will more than pay for the little bit of wheat that's lost. They won't care if they lose a little."

"I think they *will* care, William," replied Cyrus. "The farmers want a machine that cuts wheat better than it can be cut by hand. It has to cut *better* as well as faster.

"My reaper *does* cut faster, but it doesn't cut better, yet. Farmers don't lose *any* wheat when they cut it by hand."

"But you've worked on this invention for a year," William pointed out. "Aren't you even going to *try* to sell it?"

"No," Cyrus replied. "Not until I succeed in discovering a way to keep that right wheel from knocking down any wheat at all."

In the months that followed, the family always knew where to find Cyrus. He worked day and night in his little stone workshop, hammering, fitting, nailing — always trying something new.

Usually William was there too, watching. And often Mr. McCormick would stop by to ask, "Any luck, Cyrus?"

Cyrus knew how interested his father was in the reaper.

All his life, Mr. McCormick had watched farmers reap their wheat by hand, with a scythe. He knew that the thin, bow-shaped knife, fastened to a long wooden handle, was heavy and dangerous.

And he knew how hard it was to swing that heavy scythe from morning until night, one long summer day after another. Years before, Mr. McCormick himself had tried unsuccessfully to invent a reaper that would make harvesting easier.

Later, Cyrus had made up his mind to finish the reaper that his father had started. He would invent a machine that *would* be a success.

Winter passed with Cyrus still working, day after day, to make his invention better.

Spring came. The farmers planted their wheat. It grew and ripened until the golden grain was once more ready to be harvested.

One day Cyrus called his brother in and showed him a narrow board that he called a divider. "I think I've found the secret at last!" he said.

"Remember, Bill, how the grain next to the right wheel kept getting knocked down and run over last summer? Well, this new divider will push that grain out of the way so that the wheel can't harm it. Then no wheat will be wasted. See?"

"I knew you would do it!" cried William proudly. "When will you try it out?"

"Tomorrow," Cyrus said. "Tomorrow we'll take it over to John Ruff's farm and show everybody how it works."

Cyrus knew that they were hoping his invention would free them from the back-breaking work of harvesting many acres of wheat by hand.

His eyes moved down to his father, who was standing below him, next to the reaper. He knew that his father wanted this reaper to be a success as much as he did.

Mr. McCormick placed his hand on Cyrus's knee. "Good luck, son," he said softly. "I know how much this trial means to you — to all of us, in fact. Our hearts and our hopes will ride with you on your reaper."

Cyrus smiled hopefully at his father and tightened his hands on the reins. "Come on, Prince," he said to his horse. "Let's go."

The next morning, people gathered from far and near to look at Cyrus McCormick's new invention.

When everything was ready, Cyrus climbed up on the reaper and picked up his horse's reins. Then he stood, for a moment, looking out across the fields.

Acres of golden ripe grain waved gently to him in the hot summer wind. He looked at the eager, interested men sitting on the rail fence, watching, waiting, hoping.

Old Prince started down the grainfield, pulling the reaper behind him. But John Ruff's field was so bumpy that it made the reaper rock and shake as it had never done before.

People began to shout. No one could hear above the noise that the reaper was making. Then John Ruff came running up, waving wildly at Cyrus.

"Stop!" he yelled at Cyrus. "Stop, I say! This will never do! Your machine is too big and too heavy. It will knock the heads off my wheat! Stop, I say!"

The old horse stopped, and the awful noise died down. In the silence that followed, Cyrus asked, "What did you say, Mr. Ruff?"

"I said get that thing out of my wheat field!" John Ruff roared.

Cyrus was hardly able to believe his own ears. "But Mr. Ruff, we've only just started."

"No, young man, you've just finished! I'm sorry, Cyrus, but your invention just won't do! I'm afraid that it will knock down more wheat than it will cut."

Mr. McCormick came running into the field. "I think if you'll give the boy a chance, Mr. Ruff . . ." he began.

But John Ruff stood his ground. "No, thank you. I'll stick to the old way and cut my wheat with my scythe," he said.

Cyrus looked at his father helplessly. "I'm sorry, son," said Mr. McCormick. "We'll have to stop. There's nothing we can do about it." They could hear the crowd talking excitedly, and there were even a few bursts of laughter.

William came running up, hot and angry. "They called your reaper a fake!" he cried. "It's not a fake, is it?"

"No," said Cyrus. "This reaper is not a fake. It will work if it gets a fair chance."

"You're right, Cyrus," said Mr. McCormick. "Your reaper has not yet been given the fair chance that it needs."

Hearing a step behind them, they turned. William Taylor, another farmer who lived in the neighborhood, had come up in time to hear Mr. McCormick's last words.

"I'll give your invention a fair chance," he told Cyrus. "Just help me take down some of the rails of that fence, and you can lead your horse into my wheat field."

Cyrus felt as if the weight of a stone had been lifted from his heart. Eagerly he jumped back up behind old Prince and grabbed the reins again.

Mr. McCormick and William Taylor hurried toward the fence. They lifted the rails off one by one. When the opening was large enough, the horse pulled the reaper through.

As they crossed into Mr. Taylor's field, Cyrus saw that the ground there was smooth. The reaper did not rock and rattle as it had done before.

Once more he looked around him. Some of the men had left, thinking that the reaper Cyrus had invented would not work. Those who had stayed, gathered closer together, waiting for the new trial to begin.

Cyrus called to his horse, "Get up, there, Prince! Let's show them that this reaper is *not* a fake!"

Prince set off down the field, and this time they did not stop. Back and forth went the reaper, back and forth, up and down the field. By sundown, six acres of yellow wheat, cut smooth and clean, rested on the ground.

As Cyrus drew old Prince to a stop, his father and the onlookers came joyfully out to meet him.

"What a harvest!" William Taylor exclaimed. "This is a miracle, Cyrus! Your machine has done in one day the work of six men!"

"Now farmers can cut six times as much wheat without wasting *any!*" one of the other men added.

Cyrus McCormick looked at his father, his eyes shining with happiness.

"Oh, Father!" he cried. "At last our reaper is right! Now we can *really* be proud of our invention."

"I'm proud of *you*, too, son," his father said, "for doing something I couldn't do."

Cyrus held out his hand. "*You* really did it, Father," he said. "All I did was to change it a little. Just think, farmers will never again have to swing those heavy scythes!

"Let's call it McCormick, after us," Cyrus said proudly. "McCormick — that's for both of us, Father. We'll name it *THE McCORMICK REAPER.*"

Do It Right

Cyrus McCormick rebuilt his reaper again and again until, in Mr. Taylor's field, it proved to be a success. Which two of these sayings must have been in Cyrus's mind while he was rebuilding his reaper? Write two numbers.

1. The grass always looks greener on the other side of the fence.
2. What is worth doing is worth doing well.
3. A penny saved is a penny earned.
4. If at first you don't succeed, try again.

Seeing Words in Pairs

Decide how the first pair of words on each line go together. Then choose the word that should appear in each blank. Write the eight words you choose.

1. *Light* goes with *dark* as *awake* goes with __.
   (pretended, asleep, prince)
2. *Old* goes with *young* as *parent* goes with __.
   (scythe, John Ruff, child)
3. *Fast* goes with *slow* as *champion* goes with __.
   (harvest, loser, invention)
4. *Up* goes with *down* as *sunrise* goes with __.
   (grain, sunset, acres)
5. *Bought* goes with *sold* as *won* goes with __.
   (invented, lost, struggle)
6. *Hate* goes with *love* as *painful* goes with __.
   (pleasant, honest, fake)
7. *Good* goes with *bad* as *encourage* goes with __.
   (teammate, discourage, postal)
8. *Run* goes with *crawl* as *speedy* goes with __.
   (broad, slow, alphabetical)

Cyrus and George

C is a tricky letter.   In *Cyrus*, the *c* stands for the soft sound (like *s*).   In *control*, the *c* stands for the hard sound (like *k*).

The name of one of the following pictures starts with the soft sound of *c*.   Write the number of that picture on your paper.

 1.
 2.
 3.

Another letter that has both a hard and a soft sound is *g*.   The *g* in *gun* stands for the hard sound. Both *g*'s in *George* stand for the soft sound.

The name of one of the following pictures starts with the soft sound of *g*.   Write the number of that picture on your paper.

 1.
 2.
 3.

Stretching the Use of Words

On your paper write the new words you can make by adding *ed* and *ing* to each of the following words. Use each new word in a sentence.   Write the 18 sentences on your paper.

enter	peer	pretend
disappoint	appeal	succeed
treat	trust	doubt

LOOKING BACK AND REMEMBERING

Remember the People

The two lists below can be made into an outline of the stories about great people. In the left-hand list are the names of the people you have read about. The names of those people will be the five big headings of your outline.

In the right-hand list are pairs of sentences. Each pair tells about one of the persons in the left-hand list. Decide which pair of sentences should be written under each name. Make these two lists into one outline and write the outline on your paper.

I. Jane Addams   A. He loved flowers.
                           B. He wanted to learn.

II. Brother Francis   A. She founded Hull House.
                           B. She helped needy families.

III. Walter Reed   A. He invented a reaper.
                           B. He rebuilt his machine.

IV. George Washington Carver   A. He loved all animals.
                           B. He spoke kindly to a wolf.

V. Cyrus McCormick   A. He treasured his rifle.
                           B. He became a doctor.

Do You Know Your Vowel Sounds?

The first spelling in your wordbook shows how each word is divided into syllables. The respelling shows which syllable is accented most strongly.

Write the following words on your paper, showing their syllables and accents, like this: 'si·lence, in'vent. After each word show the vowel sound of the accented syllable, like this: ī.

crazy	Neosho	criticize
unto	college	carriage
trial	swallow	professor
appeal	struggle	encourage

Usually, but Not Always

When two vowels appear together, they usually stand for the long sound of the first vowel — usually, but not always. The vowel letters *ou* stand for four different sounds in the words *though, our, courage,* and *thought.*

Say the first word on each line to yourself. Listen to the vowel sound. Find another word on the line in which you hear that same vowel sound in the accented syllable. Write that word on your paper.

1. chief	supplies	shield	friend
2. sound	around	though	young
3. toe	does	shoe	Joe
4. cheat	creak	steady	break
5. choose	look	fool	floor
6. bought	group	your	fought
7. weight	neither	either	neighborhood
8. reap	dread	great	disease

Lives of great men all remind us,
We can make our lives sublime,
And, departing, leave behind us
Footprints on the sands of time.

Stories That Your Grandfather Liked

Working with Word-Builders

Would you like to know someone who is *unkind?* Would you like to know someone who always speaks *kindly* of others? Your answers to those questions show that you know the big difference in meaning between the words *kindly* and *unkind.* The word *kind* is a part of both words, yet how different they are! What makes that big difference?

A prefix (like *un-*) or a suffix (like *-ly*) changes the meaning of a word. It does this by adding its own meaning. When you know that *unkind* means *not kind,* you can guess what *unhappy, unseen,* and *undivided* mean.

You can read, understand, and use many new words when you know some of the important prefixes and suffixes in the English language. They are a part of hundreds of our everyday words. You know many of them already, in words like *gladness, truthfully, disappear, recaptured.* In the stories that follow, you will meet more of these word-builders, and you will learn more about what they can do.

The Golden Touch

Once upon a time there lived a very rich king named Midas, who loved gold more than almost anything else. He gathered together all the gold he could buy or find and locked it in an underground room of his palace.

If Midas loved anything better than gold, it was his own little daughter, Marygold. But even when she brought him buttercups, he would say, "Oh, child, if these were as golden as they look, they'd be worth picking."

Each day King Midas would go to the underground room in his palace. There, after locking the door, he would count and recount the gold money in each heavy bag.

Then he would whisper to himself, "Oh, Midas, how happy you would be if only you had all of the gold in the world."

One day when King Midas was in his treasure room, a shadow fell upon his piles of gold. Looking up quickly, he saw a stranger standing there smiling at him.

The stranger looked at all the gold in the room and then turned to King Midas. "You are a very rich man, friend Midas," he said. "I doubt that any other four walls on earth hold so much gold."

King Midas sighed aloud and shook his head. "It is not very much when you think that it has taken me my whole life to gather it together. If one could live hundreds of years he might have time to grow rich."

"What! Then you are not really happy?" exclaimed the stranger.

Again King Midas shook his head. "Would that I no longer had to work so hard to gather my treasures!" he cried. "I wish everything I touched would change into gold!"

The stranger smiled, and his smile seemed to brighten the room like sunlight. "The Golden Touch!" he exclaimed. "Are you quite sure that this would make you happy?"

"Certainly," Midas replied. "I ask nothing else to make me perfectly happy."

"Be it as you wish," said the stranger. "Tomorrow at sunrise, you will discover that you are gifted with the Golden Touch." With these words, he waved his hand and disappeared.

King Midas awoke at dawn the next morning and started to throw back his covers. But somehow, they seemed strangely heavy. To his surprise and delight, Midas saw that they had changed from white silk to cloth of gold.

Midas hurried all around the room, touching everything in sight. As soon as he put his hands upon the curtains, they hung heavy and golden at the windows. His deep purple cushions turned to the brightest gold under his touch.

He put on his clothes and was delighted to see himself in a handsome golden suit.

King Midas hurried down the stairs and out into the palace garden. The morning air was sweet with the lovely smell of many roses. Carefully, he went from bush to bush until every flower was changed to a hard, bright gold.

And then King Midas went in to breakfast and sat down at the breakfast table to wait for his beautiful little daughter Marygold.

In truth, the king loved his little daughter very much. And this morning, he loved her more than ever, because now he could give her all the gold in the world.

Soon he heard her coming along the hallway, sobbing as if her heart would break. She opened the door and came in.

"How now, my dear little lady!" cried the king. "What is the matter with you this beautiful golden morning?"

Marygold, sobbing loudly, held out a rose that Midas had changed into gold.

"It is beautiful!" exclaimed the king. "And what is there in this beautiful golden rose to make you cry?"

"Oh, my dear Father," the child answered, "it is not at all beautiful. It is the ugliest flower that ever grew." The little girl brushed away more tears as she handed the heavy golden rose to her father.

"As soon as I was up and dressed," Marygold sobbed, "I ran into the garden to gather some roses for you. But, oh dear, dear me! All the roses that used to smell so sweet are now turned quite yellow and have no smell at all."

"Well, don't you cry about it," her father said. He did not dare to tell her that he was to blame for changing the beautiful roses to hard golden flowers. "Sit down, Marygold, and eat your breakfast before it grows cold."

Midas put two beautifully browned little fish upon his plate. At once they turned to gold. Their tiny golden bones and tails were quite pretty. The king, however, would much rather have had some real fish to eat.

The king felt very, very hungry. Would he be any less hungry by lunchtime? And how would he feel by dinnertime? King Midas put his head down in his hands.

Marygold sat quietly for a moment, looking at her father. She did not understand what troubled him, but she wanted to comfort him. Midas looked so sorrowful that Marygold ran to his end of the table and hugged him close.

"My precious Marygold," her father said.

But Marygold could not reply. The moment her father touched her, Marygold's rosy face turned a shining yellow. Her soft little body grew hard within her father's arms.

Marygold was a child no longer. She was a beautiful golden statue.

And now, when it was too late, Midas knew the truth. A warm and gentle heart that loved him was worth more than all the gold on earth.

Suddenly the stranger again appeared in the room. "Well, King Midas," the stranger said, "are you happy?"

The king shook his head. "Gold is not everything," he answered sorrowfully. "I have lost the thing that my heart cared for most."

"Oh, so you have learned something since last we met," the stranger said. "Which of these two things do you now think is worth more, a piece of bread or the Golden Touch?"

"A piece of bread," said Midas, "is worth all the gold on earth."

"Would you rather have the Golden Touch," asked the stranger, "or little Marygold, warm, soft, and loving as she was an hour ago?"

"Oh, my precious child!" cried Midas. "I would not have sacrificed one hair of her head for a ball of gold the size of the whole earth!"

"You are wiser than you were, King Midas," said the stranger. "Tell me, do you truly wish to lose the Golden Touch?"

"Oh, yes! It is hateful to me," replied Midas.

"Go then," the stranger said, "and dive into the river at the bottom of your garden. Bring back a jar of water from the river, and pour the water over everything that you wish to change from gold."

The stranger disappeared.

King Midas lost no time in rushing to the river. He dived in without even taking off his golden shoes and his handsome golden suit.

When Midas came up out of the water, it gladdened his heart to see that his clothes were no longer golden. And he smiled because his shoes were only soft leather.

The king filled a large jar with water from the river and then hurried back to the palace. He carefully poured the water over the golden statue that had been Marygold.

No sooner did it fall on her, than the rosy color came back to her face.

"Stop, Father, stop!" cried Marygold. "See how you have wet my nice dress!" For the little girl did not know that she had been a golden statue.

And the king never told her. He hated the sight of gold for the rest of his life. And he never forgot that the love of his daughter was worth more than all the gold in the world.

What Good Is Gold?

Which of these lessons did Midas learn from his troubles with the Golden Touch? Write 1 or 2.

1. A golden statue can bring perfect happiness.
2. The love of a child is more precious than all the gold in the world.

Endings with Meanings

You can make two new words by adding the endings *ful* and *less* to the word *care*. *Careful* means *full of care*. *Careless* means *without care*. You can make new words also by adding *ern* to *north* and *ness* to *mad*. *Northern* means *of* or *from the north*. *Madness* means *the state of being mad*. Such endings as *ern, less, ful*, and *ness*, which can be added to a word to change its meaning, are called suffixes.

The unfinished word in each sentence below needs one of these suffixes: *ern, ful, less*, or *ness*. Decide which suffix to add in each case. On your paper write the six unfinished words, adding the right suffix to each.

1. King Midas saw the golden sun setting in the west___ sky.
2. His heart was filled with sad___ because he did not own all the gold in the world.
3. Gathering gold was an end___ job for Midas.
4. When he was first given the Golden Touch, the bright___ of gold delighted King Midas.
5. But the sight of gold soon became hate___ to him.
6. Marygold's match___ beauty gave Midas great pleasure.

A New Use for Some Words You Know

The words *up, down, over, under, in,* and *out* tell direction. When one of these words is added to the beginning of another word, it changes the meaning of the other word.

The underlined words in the sentences below can be made meaningful if you add *up, down, over, under, in,* or *out* to each. Write the six words you make.

Each morning when Marygold came (1) stairs from her bedroom in the palace tower, she would run (2) side into the garden to pick flowers. Birds flew high (3) head and sang gay songs to her.

King Midas liked to stay (4) doors in his dark (5) ground room and count his money. But some mornings he would climb back (6) stairs from his treasure room and play with Marygold in the garden.

THE LION

One day a lion was sleeping peacefully in the forest when a playful mouse, for no reason at all, ran across his outstretched paw. Then he ran up the kingly nose of the lion, awakening the great beast from his sleep.

The mighty lion caught the now frightened little creature and would have killed him, but the mouse, shivering with fear, cried out for mercy.

"Please have mercy on me, King Lion! Please don't kill me! Forgive me this time, and I will never forget it. A day may come, who knows, when I may be able to do something for you to repay your kindness."

The lion smiled at the little mouse's fright and laughed at the thought that so small a creature could ever help him. But he let the mouse go.

and the Mouse

Not long after this, the lion was caught in a net which some hunters put out in order to catch him. The angry lion let out a roar that could be heard far and wide throughout the forest.

Even the mouse heard it. He knew it was the voice of the lion that he had once made angry. And he recalled that the lion had been merciful to him then. So he ran to the place where the lion lay caught in the net of ropes.

"Well, my King," said the mouse, "I know you did not think that the day would ever come when I might repay you. But now that day is here."

The mouse set to work at once, biting with his sharp little teeth at the heavy ropes that held the lion. And soon the lion was able to crawl out of the hunters' trap and go free.

Thus did the little mouse prove to the mighty lion that an act of kindness, no matter how small, is never wasted.

From Mercy to Help

The Golden Rule tells us, "Do unto others as you would have them do unto you." Who is practicing the Golden Rule in each of these pictures? Write your answers.

1.

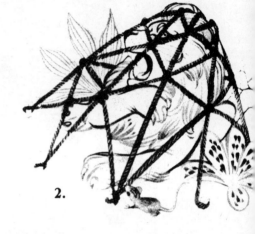

2.

From Ideas to Words

When we speak and write, words seem to pop into our minds. But they don't pop by themselves. Thus, there must first be an idea, an idea that can be made clear to someone else by means of a word.

The following meanings should make six words pop into your mind. All six of these words begin with the letters *st*. Write the six words on your paper.

1. To begin
2. A place where goods are sold
3. The likeness of a person, cut out of stone
4. The part of a tree that stays in the ground after the upper part is cut off
5. Coverings for the legs and feet
6. A car running on rails in the street

The Knights of the Silver Shield

Deep in the heart of the Forest of the Giants, there once stood a great stone castle. In this castle lived a company of knights, each of whom wore a fine suit of armor and carried a shining silver shield.

Now all these shields were magic shields. When one was new, it appeared to be cloudy. But as its owner proved himself, by word and deed, to be brave and honest, it changed from cloudy gray to brightest silver.

And the wonders of these magic shields did not end there. For it was also said that if a knight won a *very* hard battle, a golden star appeared in the center of his shield.

To win a golden star was, of course, the dearest hope of every knight. But this was very hard to do. Indeed, the lord of the castle was the only one upon whose shield a golden star could be seen.

One morning at dawn, the knights rode gaily forth to do battle with the mighty giants living in the forest. Perhaps this very day one of them would win his golden star! Everyone was excited — everyone, that is, except Sir Roland.

Roland was the youngest of all the knights. Even so, he had done many brave deeds, and his shield had a bright silver shine.

Today he had hoped that he, too, might try to win his star. But the lord of the castle had commanded that he stay at home and guard the castle gate.

"Let no one enter these gates today," he had said, and Roland had given his word to guard them well.

So now Sir Roland's heart was heavy. He stood beside the gate, watching the sunlight dance upon the armor of the knights as they galloped away.

"It does not take a brave knight to guard a castle gate," he thought. "The lord of the castle thinks I am too young to win my star. I *am* young, but that does not mean I cannot be brave and true."

But he knew that a knight must obey. He stood watching the disappearing knights until they were swallowed up by the shadows of the forest.

After a time, one of them came limping back. "I have been hurt," he said. "Let me watch the gate so that you may go back and take my place."

Now Roland could see that this man was not hurt, but was only frightened. And at first he was joyful at the thought of changing places. But then he remembered the promise he had made to the lord of the castle.

"I should like to go," he said. "But a knight belongs where his commander has placed him. So I must stay here and guard the gate myself, and you must go back to the battle."

Without another word, the man turned and walked back to the forest. Roland watched him out of sight, wishing all of the time that he could go instead.

Presently, there came an old woman down the road to the castle. She knocked loudly at the gate, and when Sir Roland looked out, she asked him for food. She looked hungry and tired, and Sir Roland knew that she truly needed his help.

"No one may enter these castle gates today," he said. "But I will send a servant out to you with food, and you may sit down and rest as long as you will."

"I have just passed the place in the forest where the fighting is going on," said the old woman as she waited.

"And how goes the battle for our brave knights?" asked Sir Roland eagerly.

"Badly, sir, I fear," replied the woman. "Those giants fight today as they have never fought before. You might better go and help your friends in the forest than to play the part of doorkeeper here."

"Indeed, I wish with all my heart that I might," said Roland. "But I am commanded to guard the castle gates, and I cannot leave. I have given my word."

"I should think that you would be much more useful out there," the old woman said.

"You may well think so," answered Sir Roland. "And so may I. But it is neither you nor I that is commander here."

"I suppose," said the old woman then, "that you are one of those who cares not for the dangers of fighting. You are lucky to have so good an excuse for staying behind."

Sir Roland was angry at this remark. It was hard to be nice to the woman when she spoke unkindly. But a knight must be kind and gentle always. So when the servant came with the food a few moments later, Sir Roland gave it to the old woman and wished her well.

Then he shut the gate, saying to himself, "She is old and tired, and I am glad that I said nothing unkind to her."

After a while, Sir Roland heard someone calling from the outside. He opened the gate and saw, standing at the other end of the drawbridge, an old man in a long black coat.

"Are you Sir Roland?" the little man called out.

"Yes," replied Sir Roland. "What do you want? The castle is closed to all comers today."

"Listen to me," said the stranger. "I have brought you a magic sword." And so saying, he drew from under his coat a wonderful sword that flashed in the sunlight.

"This is the sword of all swords," he said. "And it is for you, if you will carry it into the fight. Nothing can stand before it. When you lift it, the giants will fly before you like leaves before a wind."

Now Sir Roland had never seen a sword of such beauty. "A magic sword," he thought. "I must have it. It will help me to win my star."

He reached out his hand for it, and the little man came forward as though he would cross the drawbridge.

But at that moment, Sir Roland remembered the words of his commander. "Let no one cross the bridge today."

"Stop!" cried Sir Roland. "You may not enter the castle today, nor may I go out! Keep your sword and be gone!"

Fearing that he might yet break his promise, he touched the great bell by the gate that controlled the drawbridge.

The bridge began to rise, and as it went up, a strange thing happened. The little man threw off his black coat and began to grow taller and taller. Soon his size was a match for any giant in all the forest.

Roland trembled, then, to think what might have happened if he had left the castle gate to take the sword.

"I must be more careful," he thought. "Let me not give the lord of the castle reason to think that I am indeed too young to win my star."

Presently Sir Roland heard a sound that made him spring forward with joy.

The lord of the castle, with many of his brave knights, came riding back from the forest. They were dusty and tired, but they had won the fight with the giants. Never had there been a happier home-coming.

After he had closed the gate, Sir Roland followed the knights into the great hall of the castle.

The commander took his place. The other knights all gathered about him. Then Sir Roland came forward to report what had happened at the castle while everyone had been away fighting in the forest.

As Roland began to speak, there came a sudden stillness in the room. "Look!" one of the knights whispered. "The shield! Sir Roland's shield!" And there, shining brightly on Roland's shield, was a beautiful golden star.

"There must be a mistake!" cried Roland, who was even more surprised than the others.

"Speak, Sir Knight," said the commander. "Tell us all that has happened today. Have any giants come to the castle? Did you fight a giant alone?"

"No, my lord," said Sir Roland. "One giant came here, but he went away quietly when I would not let him enter."

Then he told how the man in the black coat had offered him a wonderful sword. "But I did not fight with him, my lord," said Roland. "I fought only with myself, to keep from breaking my promise."

When Roland had finished, there was a moment of silence. And then the lord of the castle spoke.

"A man may sometimes be mistaken," he said, "but our magic shields are never wrong. The star that we see on Sir Roland's shield proves that he has fought and won the hardest battle of us all today."

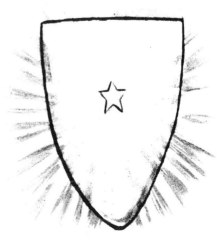

A Different Kind of Bravery

Roland earned his star by winning the hardest battle of all, the battle with himself. He wanted to put on his armor and fight the giants, but he kept command of himself and stayed at his post. Roland won his star by obeying the lord of the castle.

When you feel like disobeying, do you keep yourself under command? Answer these questions. See if you could earn your star in the way Roland earned his. Write Yes or No for each question below.

1. When your parents ask you to be home by a certain time, are you always home by then?
2. When you are playing and your mother calls you, do you go to her at once?
3. Do you eat the vegetables that your parents choose for you to eat?
4. Do you go to bed at the time set by your parents?
5. Do you follow all the directions that your teacher gives you?
6. Do you obey your school rules?
7. Do you obey safety rules when crossing the street?
8. Do you keep on watching television when your mother calls you to dinner?
9. Do you try to get out of the house without your raincoat and rubbers on cloudy days?
10. Do you talk back angrily to your parents when they say you have disobeyed?

If you could truly answer Yes to the first seven questions and No to the last three, you have earned your star.

Dictionary Reporting for Duty

Say the word *steal* to yourself. Do you hear the sound of *a* in that word? No, the only vowel sound you hear in *steal* is the long sound of *e*. Your dictionary respells *steal* like this: \\'stēl\\. This respelling tells you how to say the word.

Write the words in the left-hand list on your paper. Beside each of the words write the number of its respelling.

knight	**1.** \\'sīz\\
size	**2.** \\'sōrd\\
sword	**3.** \\'dēdz\\
deeds	**4.** \\'nīt\\

Name the Picture

The name of each picture is a compound word made by writing together a word from List A and a word from List B. On your paper write the five compounds that name the pictures.

List A	List B
butter	nails
sun	boat
finger	cup
fire	set
row	place

5.

4.

3.

2.

1.

Two Brothers from

Long, long ago, and far, far away in another land, there once lived two brothers. In peace and happiness they shared the rich and fruitful land that their father had left them.

During the warm days of early September, the brothers plowed their land. Then, row by row, they walked through the fields dropping tiny seeds of wheat into the rich, dark earth.

Through the autumn days of gentle rain and earth-warming sunshine, the green shoots of wheat pushed up tall and strong.

All winter they grew, and late in the following spring, the golden harvest was ready to be reaped.

Again the brothers walked together through the fields, cutting the golden wheat. Then they carefully gathered up the fallen grain and tied it into sheaves.

Mount Moriah

Later, in the cool of the evening after that first day's harvest, the sheaves of wheat were divided, share and share alike, between them. Then each brother placed his sheaves in a pile, and retired to his tent.

The long day's work in the sun had tired Amos, the older brother, but sleep would not come to him. He tossed on his bed, thinking of the cutting of the golden harvest that day.

Then his thoughts drifted lovingly to his younger brother, who had worked so hard beside him in the fields.

"My brother Boaz has a wife and children whose needs are many," he thought. "I have only myself and my few needs, and yet we divided the wheat, share and share alike.

"That was neither right nor fair, for Boaz and his family need more of the fruit of the land than I do."

"I have a loving wife and many willing children," thought Boaz. "When I grow old and can no longer plow the land or harvest the wheat, my strong sons will care for me.

"But Amos is all alone, and has no children to comfort him. Who will care for him in the winter of his days? My heart lies heavy, and I cannot sleep when I think of how we divided the wheat, share and share alike. That was neither right nor fair."

Then Amos arose in the night and went out toward the wheat field, dark and rustling in the moonlight. He lifted some sheaves of wheat from his pile and bore them over to his brother's pile nearby.

Then he returned to his tent and, without more trouble, he fell asleep. Throughout the night, Amos slept peacefully, happy because he had given his brother some of his wheat.

But it came to pass that a strange thing happened while Amos slept.

In the darkness of another tent, Boaz also lay sleepless, thinking of his older brother.

Boaz forthwith arose from his bed and went out to the wheat field. He lifted some sheaves of wheat from his pile and bore them to his brother's pile nearby.

At dawn the next morning, just as the first sunlight was brightening the yellow wheat field to a shining gold, the two brothers arose. Then they stood together in silence before their piles of wheat and stared with wonder.

Each of them had expected to find his pile smaller than his brother's, but each of the piles was the same size.

Neither brother spoke of this to the other. They turned silently to the field and went again about the work of reaping and harvesting their acres of golden grain.

Again, at the end of the day, they divided the sheaves, share and share alike.

But again that night, each brother arose in the darkness and went forth to bear some of his wheat to his brother's pile.

Thus, at dawn the next day, they again found that neither pile of sheaves was any greater than the other.

On the third night, both brothers arose to do again that which they had tried to do on the two nights before. But this time, Amos and Boaz met face to face as each was bearing sheaves of wheat toward his brother's pile.

They looked at each other in the moonlight, and they let the sheaves fall to the ground. They put their arms, each about the other one, and cried. They cried with joy because now they understood how great was their love for one another.

Then Boaz and Amos lifted up the wheat which they had dropped. They piled it in a special place on Mount Moriah, apart from the rest of the grain. Thus would they be reminded, when they saw it, of the love they had shown for one another.

In the course of time, a mighty king built a temple on Mount Moriah. And he placed the cornerstone of the temple on the spot where Amos and Boaz had piled their sheaves.

Thus the king hoped that the love of these two brothers would forever be remembered by all who entered the temple.

Joy on Mount Moriah

The third night that Amos and Boaz went out into the wheat field, they met one another. When they met, they cried for joy. What was the main reason that they were so happy? Write 1 or 2.

1. They understood why the size of the wheat piles had not changed.
2. They understood how great was their love for one another.

Different Letters with the Same Sound

From the following list, write the words in which you hear the sound that the word *sheep* starts with.

sheaves	machines	slept
spirit	temples	bores
precious	shoulders	share

Watch Your B's and C's

If you change the *b* to *c* in each word below, you will have five new words that name the pictures at the bottom. On your paper write each new word you make by changing *b* to *c*. After each word write the number of the picture it names.

born
block
bar
bake
boat

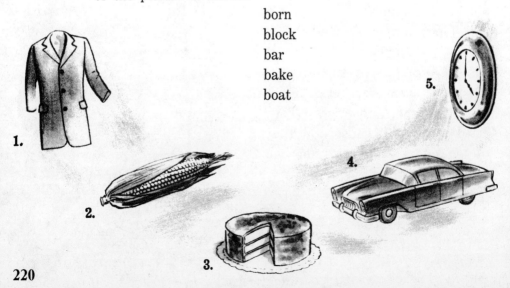

Why the Sea Is Salt

Long, long ago there were two brothers. One of them was rich and very greedy, while the other was poor, but kind and thoughtful.

It was nearly Christmas, and the weather was cold and snowy. Day and night the wind whistled around the cottage in which the poor brother lived.

There was nothing to eat in the house. It looked as if the poor man and his wife would have a very unhappy Christmas.

"Wife," said the poor man at last, "I will go to see my brother. It may be that he will give us a little food."

The rich man was angry when his brother appeared at the door to ask for food. But since it was nearly Christmas, he took down a fine ham that was hanging near the chimney.

"Take this and be gone!" he cried, throwing the ham at his brother. "I never want to see your face again!"

"Thank you, brother, for the fine ham," the poor man replied. Putting it under his arm, he started home through the snow.

On his way back through the forest, the poor brother saw an old man cutting wood.

"Good evening," said the poor brother cheerfully to the white-haired old man.

"Good evening," said the old man. "My, but that is a fine ham you have there! May I ask how you came by so good a piece of meat?"

After the way in which his brother had treated him, the poor man was quite pleased to have someone speak kindly to him. So he told the old man all about himself and his rich and greedy brother.

"It's lucky for you that you met me," said the old man. "For I can help you. You must take that ham into the land of the dwarfs. The door to their home is just under the roots of this tree.

"The dwarfs are very great lovers of ham. They will want to buy it from you. But you must not sell it for money. You must ask them for the old mill which stands behind their door. Do not take anything else for it.

"When you have the mill, come back to me and I will show you how to use it."

The poor brother thanked his new friend, and he stepped down through the door into the land of the dwarfs.

The moment that the dwarfs smelled the fine ham, they all came running.

"Give us some!" they cried. "Give us some ham! We will pay you well!"

"I will take nothing but the old mill that I saw behind the door when I entered," said the poor brother.

"No!" cried all the dwarfs. "Anything but that! Take gold! Take silver!"

The poor brother shook his head. "It seems that we cannot make a trade," he said. "So I'll be on my way. Good day."

"No, wait!" cried one of the dwarfs. "Why not let him have the mill?" he asked, turning to his fellows. "The mill is broken, anyway."

"Yes! Yes! Give him the mill!" cried the others. "We must have the ham."

So they made the trade. The poor man took the mill and went back to the old man in the woods.

"I have brought the mill," he said. "Now how shall I use it?"

"It is easy," the old man replied. "You have only to say to it, 'Grind, little mill, please grind.' Then turn the handle to the right, and the mill will grind whatever you wish."

"*Whatever I wish!*" cried the poor man. "How wonderful! But how shall I stop the mill after I have had my wish?"

"When you want it to stop, you just say, 'Thank you, little mill, thank you.'

"If you do not say 'thank you,' then the mill will keep on grinding forever. And if you do not say 'please,' then it will not grind at all.

"But the most important thing of all to remember about the mill is this. It will work only for one who does good with the riches that he gets from it. You must not be greedy. Now try it."

The poor man's hands were trembling and his voice shook as he took hold of the handle of the little mill.

"Grind, little mill, please grind," he said, and so saying, he turned the handle toward the right.

"Why, look!" he exclaimed. "A coat! Just what I wished for! Thank you, little mill, thank you!"

"Now, remember," said the old man of the woods as the mill stopped its grinding. "Do not become greedy just because the mill can supply you with whatever you wish."

As the poor brother came back to his cottage, his wife met him at the door.

"Just wait until I show you what I have here, wife!" cried the excited man. He placed the little mill on the table and said, "Grind, little mill, please grind."

His wife threw up her hands in surprise. "Look!" she said. "Look what is coming out of it! Wood for our fire! Food for our supper! Wonder of wonders, where did you get this mill?"

The poor man told her all that had happened. Then they sat by the fire and ate and ate, until the hunger they had felt before seemed as far away as a dream.

When the neighbors walked by the next day, they no longer saw the little old cottage of the poor brother. In its place stood a grand new house which the poor man had wished into being.

A few days later, the poor man, who was no longer poor, invited his brother to a feast.

"A *feast!*" exclaimed the greedy brother. "Truly, it is impossible that you mean what you say! How could *you* give a feast?"

When he arrived and saw the beautiful new house and the fine new clothes, he cried out with surprise, "What has happened? Where did you get all these fine things?"

The poor man, who was no longer poor, told his brother about the old man of the woods and about visiting the dwarfs. Then he placed the mill on the table.

"Grind, little mill, please grind," he said.

The little mill ground, and out came boots and shoes and hats and coats of all kinds and all sizes. They came out so many and so fast that they were rolling off the table.

"Good wife," said the poor man who was no longer poor, "take these things and give them to the needy people in our village. We have enough now to share with them all."

And from this day forth, the little mill began to make its owner famous for his good deeds. For he was a kind man, and he shared gladly with his neighbors all the good things which the little mill brought forth.

One day, many years later, a trader came from a land far away. His great ships were well supplied with fine goods which he hoped to trade for salt.

When the trader heard about the mill, he thought, "If I can get this mill, I will never have to sail the seas again. I can sit at home and rest, and let the little mill grind salt for me to sell."

But the poor man, who was no longer poor, would not sell the mill, not for any price.

The trader, however, would not give up the idea of owning the little mill. So he paid a servant to go and steal it for him.

Then he set sail at once. And as soon as his ship was well away from the shore, the greedy trader put the little mill to work.

"Grind, little mill," said the trader. "Please grind salt."

And the little mill began to grind. It ground and it ground and it ground.

"This is fine!" cried the trader. "Now I will become rich without ever having to work again!"

When the ship began to get full of salt, the trader turned to the mill. "Stop at once!" he commanded. But the little mill just kept on grinding.

"Stop!" the trader cried again, much louder than the first time. But the little mill did not stop.

"Stop, I say!" shouted the trader. "I have enough salt! The ship is getting full!" But still the little mill kept pouring out salt as fast as ever it could.

The trader grabbed it by the handle and shook it with all his might. "Do you hear what I say?" he shouted again. "I said to stop now. The ship is full of salt, and the deck is running over with it! Stop, or you will sink my ship!"

But the little mill did not stop. Salt rolled out faster and faster. It filled up the chairs. It piled up on the tables. It covered the deck of the ship, and then it started running down over the hull and into the water.

Finally, the weight of the salt became so great that the ship began to sink.

There was nothing that the trader could do to save himself or his men. Slowly the ship sank into the water until, at last, it completely disappeared.

So somewhere, far below the dancing waters of the sea, the faithful little mill keeps on grinding, grinding, grinding. And from this mill, the salt keeps pouring, pouring, pouring. And this, as you might easily guess, is why the sea is salt.

Know Them by Their Acts

Why the Sea Is Salt tells about two brothers who were quite different. One was greedy and hateful. The other was kind and good.

In the pictures below you see only the backs of the two brothers. But you can still tell which brother is in which picture by what he is doing.

On your paper write the numbers of the pictures in which you see the kind brother.

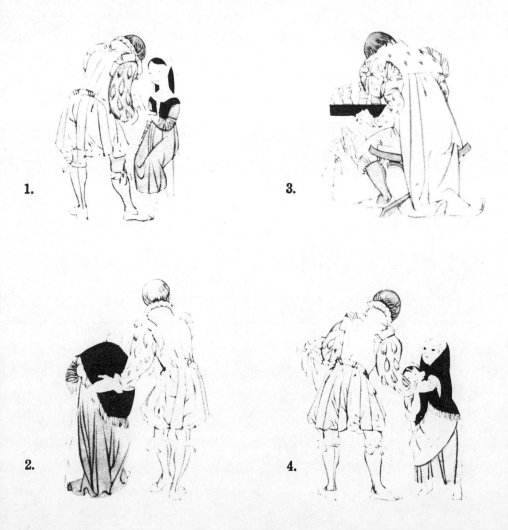

1.

3.

2.

4.

More and Most

Write the two missing words on your paper.

If *sadder* always means *more sad,*
And *madder* has to mean *more mad,*
Then anyone who knows the score
Should see that *e-r* can mean ___.

If *maddest* means *most mad of all,*
And *saddest, sad enough to bawl,*
You've very little cause to boast
If you know *e-s-t* means ___.

More Pairs of Words

On your paper write the word that should appear at the end of each sentence.

1. *Saying* goes with *speaking* as *fighting* goes with ___.
    (sinking, battling, bawling)
2. *Lovely* goes with *pretty* as *precious* goes with ___.
    (greedy, dear, grinding)
3. *Terrible* goes with *awful* as *quiet* goes with ___.
    (sank, slept, silent)
4. *Large* goes with *giant* as *small* goes with ___.
    (sheaves, unto, dwarf)
5. *Sweet* goes with *sugar* as *bright* goes with ___.
    (sunshine, suffix, errand)
6. *Brave* goes with *knight* as *sharp* goes with ___.
    (deed, sword, armor)
7. *Flower* goes with *rose* as *animal* goes with ___.
    (compound, main, wolf)
8. *Fruit* goes with *apple* as *meat* goes with ___.
    (ham, medicine, vinegar)
9. *Bird* goes with *robin* as *grain* goes with ___.
    (size, jeans, wheat)

LOOKING BACK AND REMEMBERING

Unusual Stories

Which story told about each of the following? Write your answers.

1. a. Two brothers who were alike
   b. Two brothers who were different
2. a. A magic touch
   b. A magic shield
3. a. The Golden Rule as practiced by animals
   b. The Golden Rule as practiced by brothers
4. a. A trader who was greedy
   b. A king who was greedy

Rhymes for Remembering

Answer the questions about each rhyme.

> King Midas cried, "My child is much
> More precious than the Golden __."

1. What word is needed to finish the rhyme?
2. In what word do you hear the hard sound of *c*?
3. On which syllable of the king's name does the accent fall?

> The magic mill would grind until
> Someone said, "Thank you, little __."

1. What word is needed to finish the rhyme?
2. Which word is a compound?
3. In what word do you hear the soft sound of *g*?

> Though Sir Roland didn't fight,
> He proved himself the bravest __.

1. What word is needed to finish the rhyme?
2. Which word stands for *did not?*
3. Which word ends with three letters that mean *most?*

What You Can Do with a Word

You have now learned many prefixes and suffixes that can be added to a word to change its meaning. The following letters should be added to the word *play* to make the words needed in the sentences below.

Endings	Prefixes	Suffixes
's	*re*	*er*
ed	*out*	*ful*
ing		*fulness*

On your paper write the word needed in each blank.

1. Yesterday Jack __ with his dog for an hour.
2. His mother said, "Please stop __ with your dog and come to dinner."
3. Jack's dog always felt __.
4. This morning the dog was so full of __ that he started running after his tail.
5. Jack was the best __ on the baseball team.
6. Since the team had used the wrong set of rules, they had to __ the game.
7. A well-trained team that has practiced a lot can __ a lazy team.
8. Jack made a long speech in the __ first act.

You know how to use many forms of the word *play* in sentences. But do you know how each prefix and suffix changes the meaning of *play*?

Write the following words on your paper. Beside each word write the number of its meaning.

playful	1.	to play again
replay	2.	one who plays
playfulness	3.	full of play
outplay	4.	the state of being playful
player	5.	to play better than

A PRAYER

Father, we thank thee for the night
And for the pleasant morning light,
For rest and food and loving care,
And all that makes the world so fair.
Help us to do the things we should,
To be to others kind and good,
In all we do, in all we say,
To grow more loving every day.

Stories of Other Days

Looking Back

Going over what you have learned can often be helpful, since "practice makes perfect." The sentences below are a reminder of facts and rules you have been working with. But be careful! Not all of the sentences are true. Read them and decide which three *are* true. Then decide which one has been respelled at the end.

1. There is a letter for every sound.
2. Sounds, syllables, and accent are all important in saying words.
3. Silent-*e* words usually have a long vowel sound.
4. Letters can fool you, because one letter may stand for several sounds.
5. Prefixes and suffixes both come at the ends of words.

\ˈlet-rz kən ˈfül ˈyü bə-ˈkȯz ˈwən ˈlet-r ˈmā ˈstand fər ˈsev-r-əl ˈsaùndz\

Now go on to the last stories, and \in-ˈjȯi t͟həm ˈȯl\!

The Best Kiter

One day, over a hundred years ago, a boy named Homan Walsh sat staring down at a swift and dangerous river, roaring along below.

As he watched the rushing waters of the Niagara River come crashing down over the Niagara Falls, he was trying to picture a bridge.

It would stretch from the cliffs of the United States, where he was sitting, to the high stone walls of Canada, across the river.

Homan's mind was filled with wonder. Could a bridge like that really be built? It seemed impossible. And yet, just an hour before, he had heard a man say that the plans for starting such a bridge had already been made.

What they needed, first, the man had said, was to get a string across from one side of the river to the other. It seemed that the best way this could be done was by flying a kite across.

So a five-dollar prize was going to be given to the first person to succeed in doing this.

Five dollars! My, what a wonderful prize! Homan stood up and stared across at the steep cliffs on the Canada side of the river. How wonderful it would be if the string of *his* kite could be the first to bridge this great, wide gap!

"I'm sure I can do it!" he cried out suddenly, jumping to his feet. And as Homan spoke, the river seemed to catch his words and roar back, "Do it! Do it!"

So Homan Walsh ran home to build a new kite.

Homan already had several kites which he had built himself. But he wanted *this* kite to be something special. And as he worked on it that afternoon, he tried to think of a name for his new kite.

Homan thought about the speech Mr. Ellett had made. He was the engineer who was offering the five-dollar prize.

"When we get that kite string across, it will be the first real link between Canada and the United States," Mr. Ellett had said. "The bridge that we build will bring about a much closer union between the two countries."

Suddenly a big grin spread across Homan's face. At last he had found the right name for his kite! In large, black letters, he carefully wrote across the kite, "UNION."

Homan's father smiled when he saw the new kite. "That's a mighty ambitious name to give a kite!" he said with a smile.

"Well, this kite is a mighty ambitious one!" Homan said proudly. "It hopes to fly all the way over to Canada and win a five-dollar prize for me!"

Mr. Walsh shook his head doubtfully. "I've heard about Mr. Ellett's idea for the bridge. Sounds crazy to me!"

"I don't understand," said Homan's mother. "What does this kite you just made have to do with building a bridge, Homan?"

"After they get the kite string across, they'll fasten a heavier string to it, then a rope, and then a cable," Homan explained. "Then they will pull a big basket back and forth on the cable while they build the bridge between Canada and the United States."

"Imagine riding to Canada in a basket!" said Mrs. Walsh.

"Well, I don't think that it can be done," said Homan's father. "And I think you'll be wasting your time, Homan, if you bother trying to win Mr. Ellett's prize."

"Maybe," said Homan. "But as long as Mr. Ellett thinks it's worth trying, I hope my kite will be the one to win!"

The next day there was a strong wind. Homan went out with the other boys to try for Mr. Ellett's prize. Their bright kites whirled into the wind, up toward the clouds.

But sailing a kite across the Niagara was harder to do than Homan had expected.

Just when Union seemed to be doing well, the wind would change, and Homan would feel his kite being pressed back down again.

Now and then, kite lines would become tangled up with one another, or a kite would drop into the river.

Finally Homan pulled in his kite and went back to the place where Mr. Ellett stood.

"Are you giving up?" asked the engineer.

"Not I!" said Homan with a quick grin. "But the wind blows from Canada most of the time. So I'm going to try flying my kite from that side."

"That's a good idea!" said Mr. Ellett, giving Homan a pat on the back. "We'll watch for Union over here."

The next morning was clear and sunny. Homan got up early, packed his kiting supplies, and asked his mother to fix a lunch for him.

Then he walked from his home to the top of the cliffs near Niagara Falls. Holding Union in one hand, he climbed carefully down the long, steep trail to the boat landing at the river's edge below.

The roaring waters were swift and dangerous, but the rivermen here knew the Niagara well. It did not take long for one of the boats to carry Homan over to Canada.

Once there, he climbed up another steep trail and walked along the cliff for two miles.

He stopped at Johnny Wells' house and asked his friend to come along. Then they hurried on together to the spot where Homan planned to send his kite across the river.

When they arrived, they found that several other boys were there already and had the same idea.

"Here she goes!" Homan shouted, letting out his string. Up, up went Union, and headed toward the other shore.

After several hours, Homan asked Johnny to hold the string while he ate his lunch.

The wind blew more and more fiercely as the day wore on, and one by one the other boys gave up and went home.

When Johnny went home for supper, late that afternoon, Homan stayed on alone. He was hoping that the wind would die down and drop his kite on the opposite shore.

Suddenly he felt a change in the pull of his string, and he began at once to wind it in. But then he felt another sharp pull, and the string went limp.

His kite had landed at the foot of the cliffs on the opposite shore. But the kite string had caught on an ice cake in the river and had snapped in two. So all the hard work of that long, cold day had been done for nothing!

Homan felt terribly tired. The sky looked dark and stormy. There was no prize in sight as he climbed down to cross the river and find his kite.

A few days later, Homan started out again. When he reached the boat, the riverman did not want to make the trip. The Niagara was full of ice.

"Please," begged Homan. "I'm not afraid. It's awfully important that I get across."

Then the riverman looked at the boy with the kite in his arms and replied, "All right, young fellow. We'll give it a try!"

Huge blocks of ice knocked against the little boat as it bounced bravely along over the icy water. But they made the trip safely.

Homan almost ran up the steep trail on the Canada side. Within a few minutes, he had Union sailing toward the blue skies above the cliffs on the opposite shore.

It was a beautiful, clear morning, and Homan's spirits sailed up, up, up and danced with his kite in the sky.

Suddenly the kite dropped. At once Homan started to pull in the line. For one dreadful moment, he thought Union was going to drop into the whirlpool below. But then it lifted again, just enough.

Across the river, he saw people running and reaching for his kite. Now arms were waving joyfully at him. Union had made the crossing!

There were tears of joy in Homan's eyes when Mr. Ellett handed him the five dollars.

"Here's the prize, Homan," Mr. Ellett said kindly. "And you have certainly earned every penny of it! But your biggest prize will be to know, after the bridge is built, that *you* made the link that will never be broken."

Try, Try Again

Homan worked hard to fly his kite across the Niagara River and make a link between Canada and the United States. He wanted his kite string to be the first step toward the bridge that would stretch across the gap between the countries.

Homan would let nothing stop him from getting Union across. Even when the fierce wind was tangling kite lines and blowing in the wrong direction, Homan did not give up. He kept trying until he landed Union on the other side.

On your paper write what Homan did when each of these troubles arose:

1. The wind blew in the wrong direction on his side of the river.
2. Just as his kite landed across the river, the string caught on a huge ice cake and snapped.
3. A few days later, the river became icy and dangerous to cross.

Playing Word Games

Match the words that have opposite meanings. Write the six pairs of opposites on your paper.

enemy   tiny
neither   lived
died   friend
huge   both
frown   hate
love   smile

The Best Loser

Many boys could try for Mr. Ellett's five-dollar prize, but only one boy could win it. Homan won the prize because he was the best kiter.

If you had been one of the other kiters, how would you have felt when Homan won? Would you have been angry because you did not win? Would you have decided never to try for a prize again? Or would you have been a good sport and acted pleasant even though you were disappointed?

Which two of the following sentences tell how a good loser feels and acts? Write two numbers on your paper.

1. He feels unhappy, but he acts cheerful.
2. He feels unhappy, and he acts angry.
3. He feels disappointed, and he acts unpleasant.
4. He feels disappointed, but he acts pleasant.

Rhymes That Need Your Help

The last word is missing from each of the rhymes below. On your paper write the four words that belong in the four blanks.

1. The river was dangerous, narrow, and deep;
   The cliffs that were standing beside it were __.
2. A prize of five dollars would surely excite
   Any boy who was clever at flying a __.
3. When naming his kite, Homan started to think
   That a bridge between countries is quite a good __.
4. His father thought no one would ever be able
   To cross the swift stream in a basket by __.

How the Little Kite Learned to Fly

"I never can do it," the little kite said,
As he looked at the others high over his head;
"I know I should fall if I tried to fly."
"Try," said the big kite, "only try!
Or I fear you never will learn at all."
But the little kite said, "I'm afraid I'll fall."
The big kite nodded: "Ah, well, good-by;
I'm off." And he rose toward the cloudless sky.
Then the little kite's paper stirred at the sight,
And trembling, he shook himself free for flight.
First whirling and frightened, then braver grown,
Up, up he rose through the air alone,
Till the big kite, looking down, could see
The little one rising steadily.

Then how the little kite thrilled with pride,
As he sailed with the big kite side by side!
While far below he could see the ground,
And the boys, like small spots moving round.
They rested high in the quiet air,
And only the joyful birds were there.
"Oh, how happy I am!" the little kite cried,
"And all because I was brave, and tried."

Riding the Pony Express

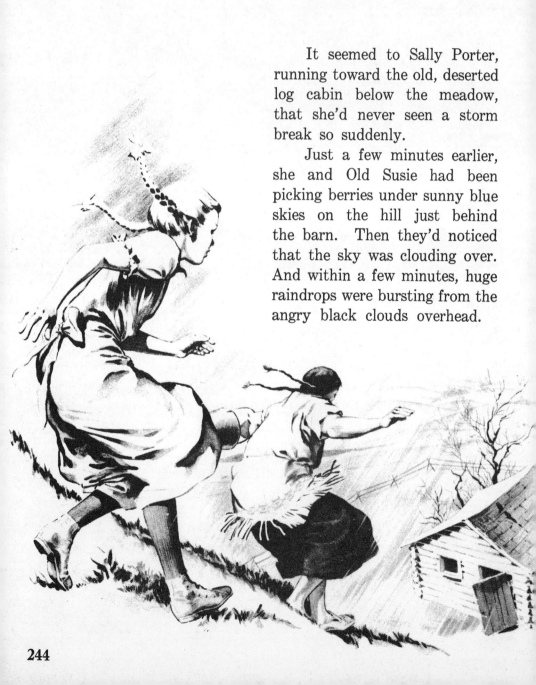

It seemed to Sally Porter, running toward the old, deserted log cabin below the meadow, that she'd never seen a storm break so suddenly.

Just a few minutes earlier, she and Old Susie had been picking berries under sunny blue skies on the hill just behind the barn. Then they'd noticed that the sky was clouding over. And within a few minutes, huge raindrops were bursting from the angry black clouds overhead.

Now Sally followed the old Indian woman across the clearing. Old Susie was nearly as broad as she was tall, but she moved with surprising speed.

As they entered the empty cabin, a new cloudburst sent buckets of rain pouring down from the sky. Old Susie shut the door against the storm.

Only the light that crept in through the cracks between the logs kept it from being pitch black within the cabin. In the darkness, Sally could imagine the grin on Susie's face as she said, "Good thing Old Susie know short cut, yes?"

Sally was still breathing heavily from their run. "Oh, yes!" she exclaimed.

But she couldn't help wishing that Old Susie had known of a short cut home instead of a short cut to this cabin. For every minute that passed would be bringing her brother Andy closer and closer to home.

Sally's mother had gone to help a sick neighbor. Now that Sally was trapped up here by the rain, there would be no one at home to meet Andy.

He would not be able to wait around for someone to get back there, either.

He would stop only long enough to throw the heavy mail pouches from the tired horse he was riding to a fresh one. Then he'd be off again on the last leg of his ride before turning the mail over to the next Pony Express rider.

Sally's spirits sank when she peered out at the driving rain through one of the cracks between the logs.

All at once something else caught her eye. Two men had come into sight at the far edge of the clearing and were heading hurriedly toward the cabin.

Old Susie saw them, too. Quickly she grabbed Sally and half pulled, half pushed her down into a corner.

Then she dragged an old packing box and a broken chair in front of them. "Black Jack come," she whispered, sinking to the floor beside Sally. "Him bad. We hide."

Before Sally could reply, the door was thrown open, and the two men stumbled in.

"Lucky you knew this place was here, Jack!" exclaimed the smaller of the two men, shaking off the rain like a wet dog.

"Pays to know the hideouts in these parts," answered the other man, leaning against the open doorway. "This is as good a place as any to talk.

"Now Andy Porter will be coming through here at about four-thirty. He'll be carrying a lot of money this trip. I plan to stop him at Big Rock."

"But, Jack," the other man said, "that's U.S. mail!"

"It's only the money I'm after," said Black Jack. "If he hands that over, he can keep his precious mail. If he doesn't . . ." Black Jack lifted his shoulders.

Sally stirred worriedly in the darkness, but Old Susie's fingers pressed tight into her knee, warning her to be silent.

"There's just one chance that things might go wrong," added Black Jack. "And that's the reason you're in on this. Andy may take the cutoff back of his place.

"If he does take it, he'll come out just below the Gap. You wait there."

"O.K.," the smaller man said. "I'll shoot him as he comes onto the trail."

Black Jack went on. "I may have trouble crossing the river, with all this rain. But wait for me. And I'm warning you, *don't let him get by*. If you do, there'll be a dead man at the Gap, and I don't mean Andy Porter!

"Now let's get going. The rain's letting up."

After the men had gone, Old Susie held Sally back until she thought it was safe. When Susie finally said, "All right, Sally, go now," Sally almost flew down the mountain toward home.

She built up a fire with trembling hands. Then she put on a pot of coffee and pushed a pan of half-baked rolls into the warm stove.

It seemed no time at all before she heard Andy's wolf howl, the signal he always gave as he came down the trail.

Sally met him down by the corral and poured out her story excitedly. Andy listened while he dragged his saddle and his blanket from the back of the tired horse.

Then they hurried into the house, and he quickly swallowed the hot coffee that Sally had ready for him.

"Good girl!" Andy said with a smile, stuffing Sally's rolls into a leather pouch that hung over his deerskin shirt. "Now you must listen carefully. I'm going to take the cutoff trail behind the house. I was planning to, anyway, because of this storm.

"Besides, I'd rather face that other man on the upper trail than Black Jack at Big Rock. Black Jack is too good a shot."

Sally put out her hand to stop him, but he shook it off.

"I was expecting trouble on this run because I'm carrying so much money," he added.

"The pouches that usually carry the mail are now stuffed with fake letters. The real mail is rolled up in that blanket behind my saddle, and all the Express money is sewed into the saddle lining.

"When the man stops me, I'll throw him the pouches and hope that it fools him. If it works, I may get through."

Andy gave Sally the empty cup and hurried outside. "You can see the Gap from here, Sal. Usually I make it in twenty minutes. The mud will slow me down, so give me thirty minutes this time. Saddle your horse as soon as I leave.

"Stand outside where you can see clearly. I'll wave my hat when I reach the Gap. If you don't see me ride through that Gap within thirty minutes, you're to take the cutoff and find out why."

Andy patted his sister on the shoulder.

Then he turned his horse, jumped into the saddle, and galloped away.

Sally saddled her horse. Then she put on an old pair of Andy's pants and a leather shirt and tucked her curls up into one of Andy's hats.

As Sally dressed, she was careful to keep an eye on the window that looked toward the Gap. And at the end of every minute, she turned her father's little minute glass upside down.

When there were just five minutes to go, she walked her horse out to the gate, from which she could see the Gap clearly. But still Andy did not ride through.

Five times more, she turned the minute glass. Then she jumped on her horse and started up the cutoff trail.

She found Andy on the trail below the Gap. The short man she had seen at the cabin lay face down in the mud. Andy's horse was dead.

Andy lay on the ground beside his horse. He was trying without success to untie the blanket that had the mail in it. He had fastened a leather band about his leg, and above this, his trousers were bright with blood.

As Sally's horse rounded the last curve, Andy whirled about, grabbing his gun from the ground beside him.

"Oh, Sal!" he cried. "Am I glad that it's you! You're in time. Here, get this mail off my pony and onto yours. Never mind anything else. We can't get the saddle off. The horse is lying on it.

"Ride for all you're worth into Placer City. Turn the mail over to Johnson at the Pony Express Station there and tell him what happened."

"But you're hurt!" cried Sally. "Look at all that blood! I can't leave you lying here like this."

"You're to do as I say," Andy ordered. "Change this blanket over. Get going."

Before Sally could object again, someone slipped out of the woods behind them. Sally's heart jumped as she whirled around, expecting to find herself face to face with Black Jack.

"Old Susie!" cried Andy. "Boy, am I glad to see *you!*"

"How did you know where to come?" asked Sally.

"Susie hear." The Indian woman stooped down and lifted Andy like a bag of corn across her shoulder. Then she bore him off into the trees and came back carrying Andy's gun.

Old Susie handed the gun to Sally. With one swing of her strong arms, she pulled the saddle off Sally's horse.

Then she pushed and pulled at the dead horse until she had freed Andy's saddle. Together, she and Sally put the saddle on Sally's horse and tied the blanket tightly behind.

Sally tried to make her trembling hands work fast. She kept looking down toward the trail from Big Rock, expecting Black Jack to appear at any moment.

"Black Jack come by and by," said Old Susie.

"I wonder what's keeping him?" Sally said.

Old Susie smiled. "Horse gone," she said. "He tie horse by tree. He go sit Big Rock. Susie chew reins off horse. Give horse big hit behind."

Sally quickly pulled herself up into the saddle. "Good Old Susie!" she laughed. Susie grinned proudly and waved at Sally. And Sally waved back as she dug her heels into her horse's sides and started up the steep road toward the Gap.

Two hours later, she came galloping into Placer City and up to the Pony Express Station.

"Thought you'd never get here!" shouted the angry voice of the waiting rider. "You're an hour late." And then, "Well, well. It isn't Porter. It's a girl. Who are *you?*"

"I'm Andy's sister," said Sally, sliding out of the saddle. "There was a holdup. Andy was hurt, and he couldn't ride. The money's sewed inside the saddle, and the mail is rolled up in the blanket."

Her knees were trembling. She could hardly stand.

The rider stared hard at her for a moment. Then, with a practiced hand, he slid the saddle onto his fresh horse and carefully tied the blanket on behind it.

"You did all right, girl!" he exclaimed, swinging himself into the saddle. "Yes, sir, you did right well, for a first try, riding for the Pony Express!"

Duty First

Andy always did his duty, no matter how dangerous that duty happened to be. Which two of these facts about Andy show that he really believed in doing his duty? Write the numbers on your paper.

1. He gave a wolf howl as he rode up the trail.
2. When Sally told him that Black Jack and a gunman were waiting for him, he decided to ride with the mail, anyway.
3. He drank the coffee Sally had made for him.
4. When he was hurt, he sent Sally on with the mail to the next Pony Express Station.

A Quiz About Meanings

After each sentence are two meanings for the underlined word in that sentence. Write on your paper the letter of the meaning it has in the sentence.

1. Low-hanging rain clouds blanketed the valley.
   a. Wrapped in warm, heavy cloth
   b. Covered
2. Black Jack stormed into the cabin.
   a. Came in noisily
   b. Brought a rainstorm with him
3. Fear bit into Sally's heart when she heard Black Jack talking.
   a. Entered
   b. Cut with teeth
4. Andy steeled himself to face the danger of meeting the gunman.
   a. Made himself be brave and strong
   b. Put on a steel shirt

What Happened Where?

a.

b.

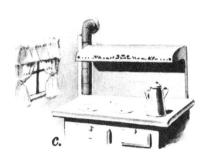

c.

d.

These four pictures show four places that were told about in *Riding the Pony Express*. The sentences below tell things that happened in these four places. In which place did each thing happen? On your paper write the number of each sentence and the letter of the picture that matches it.

1. Sally reports the holdup.
2. Old Susie stoops down, lifts Andy, and carries him into the woods.
3. Old Susie and Sally run inside when buckets of rain start pouring down.
4. Andy stuffs Sally's rolls into his pouch.
5. Old Susie drags an old packing box in front of herself and Sally.
6. Sally watches the Gap to see if Andy will ride through.
7. A Pony Express rider takes the mail which Sally has brought.
8. Sally sees the blood on Andy's trousers and notices that his horse is dead.

INDIANS IN THE HOUSE

Early one morning, Pa took his gun and went hunting. He had meant to make a bed today and had brought in the boards.

But then Ma had told him that there was no meat in the house for dinner. So he stood the boards against the wall and took down his gun.

Jack barked at him. He wanted to go hunting, too. His eyes begged Pa to take him, but Pa chained him to the barn.

"No, Jack," Pa had said. "You must stay here and guard the place." Then he turned to his two little daughters, Laura and Mary, and said, "Don't let Jack loose, girls."

Poor Jack! He hated to be chained. He sank to the ground and lay there with his sad eyes turned away from Pa. He would not watch Pa going away without him.

But the two girls waved to Pa as he went away. They watched as he grew smaller and smaller, until the huge prairie swallowed him and he was gone.

Then Laura stooped down and tried to comfort Jack, by petting him and scratching him behind his ears.

All day long, Laura and her sister stayed near the barn, trying to cheer up their dog.

Jack's head was resting on Laura's knees, and she was talking to him, when suddenly he stood up and gave a deep, low growl. The hair on his neck stood straight up, and his eyes looked wild and angry.

Laura was frightened. She had never heard the dog growl in that way before. Then she looked over her shoulder, and her·blood seemed to turn cold inside of her.

Two very tall, fierce-looking men were coming swiftly along the trail. Their bare skin was brownish-red. The shiny black hair on their heads seemed to stand straight up, ending in a tower of bright feathers.

"Indians!" Laura whispered. "Look, Mary, they're coming toward the house!" Laura was so frightened that the words seemed to stick in her throat.

The two men came closer and closer. Then both of them disappeared beyond the other side of the house.

But they did not come into sight again, as they should have if they had kept on walking. They must have entered the house!

Laura was in a fever of fear, now. There was a queer feeling in her middle, and her legs felt too weak to hold the weight of her body.

"Mary," Laura whispered, "they must be in the house with Ma and Baby Carrie!"

All this time, Jack had been growling fiercely. Now he stopped growling and pulled wildly against the chain, trying to get loose.

"I think we'd better let Jack loose," Laura whispered. "He'll kill those Indians. It's the only way to help Ma."

"But Pa told us not to," Mary answered.

"Pa didn't know Indians would come," Laura said.

"But he still said for us not to let Jack loose." Mary was almost crying.

Laura turned toward the house. "Well," she said, "if we can't let Jack go help Ma, we'll have to do it ourselves."

But she did not feel as brave as she sounded. She ran two steps and walked a step. Then she turned and flew back to the dog, throwing her arms fiercely about his strong neck.

She hugged him hard for a moment. Then she made her arms let go and ran toward the house as fast as she could.

Mary stayed close behind her. When they reached the door, it was standing open, so they slipped into the house without a sound.

The two Indian braves were standing by the fireplace. They did not seem to be hurting Ma at all. She was stooping over the fireplace, cooking something. The baby held onto Ma's skirt with both hands, hiding her head in the big apron.

The faces of the red men were fierce and terrible. Their black eyes were shining. Both Indians were looking straight at Laura!

Her heart jumped into her throat and choked her with its pounding. She stood there, as still as a statue.

The cornbread Ma had made was ready now, and she put it on the table. Without speaking, the Indians sat down and started to eat.

Ma stood and watched them, smoothing Baby Carrie's curls with trembling hands.

When every scrap of cornbread had been stuffed into their mouths, the two Indians stood up and spoke to Ma in their own language. Then they walked out of the house.

Ma sighed a long, long sigh. Then she sat down on the bed and pulled little Carrie up beside her. Ma was still all trembly, and she looked sick.

"Do you feel sick, Ma?" Mary asked her.

"No," Ma replied weakly. "I'm just glad they're gone."

Then they told her how they had left Jack and come into the house to help her and Baby Carrie.

Ma patted their hands and called them "her brave girls."

"Now we must get dinner," she said. "Pa will be wanting a good meal when he comes."

Laura was the first to see Pa returning. He was carrying a rabbit and two prairie hens.

Before he could even put them down, Laura and Mary ran up and grabbed him, both talking at once.

"What's this?" he asked. "Indians? So, at last you've seen some Indians, have you? I noticed a new camp not far from here. But did Indians really come to the house?"

"Yes, two of them," Ma replied. "I'm sorry, but they ate a lot of cornbread. They pointed to the cornmeal and made signs for me to cook some. I was afraid not to."

"You did the right thing," Pa told her. "We don't want to make enemies of any Indians."

"But we were short of cornmeal," Ma said.

"Never mind," Pa replied. "We can get more meal when we go for our supplies. It's a small enough sacrifice to make in order to keep peace with the Indians.

"Come on, now, Laura and Mary. You girls can watch me skin the rabbit and dress the prairie hens while Ma gets the coffee ready."

As they sat on the woodpile, watching Pa work with his hunting knife, Laura was still thinking about the two Indians. "Pa," she exclaimed suddenly, "if we had let Jack loose, he'd have eaten those Indians right up, wouldn't he?"

Pa laid down his knife. "Laura," he said quietly, "did you really think of turning him loose, even after I had told you not to?"

Laura swallowed hard, looking at the ground. "Well, Pa," she said weakly, "we were so afraid that the Indians would hurt Ma and Baby Carrie."

Pa was quiet for a moment. Then he sighed a long sigh, like Ma's sigh after the two Indians had gone away.

"Girls," he said, as he took both of their little hands in his two big ones, "I'm not going to scold you. You were frightened, and sometimes it's hard to know what's best to do when you're afraid.

"But you might have done Ma and Carrie and all the rest of us a lot of harm if you had disobeyed me. Do you know what would have happened if you had turned Jack loose?"

"I guess Jack would have tried to bite them, wouldn't he?" Laura asked.

"Yes, he certainly would!" said Pa. "And those Indians probably wouldn't have liked that at all. It might very well have caused trouble between the Indians and us settlers — bad trouble.

"Now I know it isn't always easy to do as I've told you," Pa went on. "But I only tell you to do what I think will be best *for everybody*.

"I hope you'll think of that the next time you want to do something I've said not to. It may help you to remember that there are lots of things that are worse than friendly Indians in the house."

Think Before You Act

Laura and Mary were so frightened when they saw the Indians that they wanted to disobey their father and let Jack loose. The girls did not stop to think what the Indians would do if Jack bit one of them.

Which picture shows what might have happened if Laura and Mary had let Jack attack the Indians? Write 1 or 2 on your paper.

1.

2.

An Accent Trick

Here are two sentences with the word *present*.

1. Let me present the prize to the winner.
2. The winner was given a lovely present.

On which syllable of *present* does the accent fall in the first sentence? On which syllable of *present* does the accent fall in the second sentence? As you see, you can sometimes change the meaning of a word by putting the accent on a different syllable.

The words *object* and *desert* should be used to fill the blanks in the following four sentences.

On your paper write the word that should appear in each blank. After it, write *first* or *second* to show which syllable should be accented.

1. The prairie was as flat as a bare, sandy __.
2. "We can't __ Ma. She needs us," cried Laura.
3. "I __ to the way the Indians acted," said Ma.
4. The Indians carried a strange-looking __ to their camp.

Quiz Questions

On your paper write the answer to each question.

In which *one* of these words do you hear the short sound of *a* as in *drag?*

      bawl   sank   Laura

In which *two* of these words do you hear the short sound of *i* as in *blink?*

      sink   link   grind

In which *one* of these words do you hear the long sound of *i* as in *giant?*

      Niagara   Carrie   skirt

In which *one* of these words do you hear the short sound of *e* as in *press?*

      Ellen   fierce   weak

In which *one* of these words do you hear the sound of *o* as in *form?*

      unto   boast   order

In which *two* of these words do you hear the sound of *th* as in *thus?*

      whether   scythe   thirsty

In which *two* of these words do you hear the sound of *sh* as in *shirt?*

      chain   machine   precious

Giving Is Thanks

On a winter afternoon of the year 1621, a young Indian boy paddled swiftly toward a stretch of sandy shore.

Morning Bird had just left the place in the forest where nearly a hundred braves of his father's tribe were camped.

Next morning, he would go with them to the village of the white men for a feast. It was to be a feast to give thanks for the first grain which the white men had harvested since coming to this land.

Massasoit, Morning Bird's father, and chief of the tribe, had taken his braves hunting. They had killed five large deer, which they planned to bring to the white men as their share of the feast.

Now Morning Bird slid his canoe, as lightly as the brush of a feather, onto the sand. Then he climbed up along the path which led to the edge of the woodland near the white men's village.

Morning Bird had come to this place many times before. Silently he had hidden in the bushes to watch these strange people going about among their queer little houses.

He had also seen the ship in which they had sailed across the sea. It rested upon the water like a great white bird. When he first caught sight of it, Morning Bird had thought it was a giant canoe with wings.

Four moons later, the ship had gone away, but these brave people had not gone with it.

Morning Bird came to the edge of the woods and looked down into the village. It was the time of cold weather, and smoke was rising from all the chimneys of the houses.

Several hunters, with their wild turkeys thrown across their shoulders, were walking into the settlement. Young children ran laughing to meet them, and women came and stood in the doorways of their houses.

It was like the return of his own tribesmen from a hunting trip, thought Morning Bird.

He stretched out carefully behind the screen of dry and tangled underbrush to watch the people of the settlement.

A boy of about his own age was putting up markers on a tree trunk. There would be games tomorrow. Morning Bird thought proudly that he would show this white boy how an arrow could be driven into the center of the mark.

The door of a house below opened, and a girl came out carrying a bucket. She turned toward the spring, which was within a stone's throw of where Morning Bird lay hidden.

Her small feet bore her lightly over the hard ground, and as she ran, her fair hair streamed behind her in the wind.

Morning Bird had never seen hair like the hair of this girl. It was like the touch of sunlight on a golden-feathered bird, or like the far-off glowing of a bright, bright star.

The Indian boy sat staring, as still as the woods around him. Only his eyes moved as he watched the girl stoop to fill her bucket at the spring.

All the other children of the settlement, with their white faces and colorless costumes, were like the small, gray snowbirds. But this girl had hair of gold, like a daughter of the Sun God.

The girl set her bucket on the ground and seated herself on a smooth rock. Lifting her left foot, she took off her shoe and shook a small stone out of it. Then she sat rubbing her foot, with a little hurt sound coming from her mouth.

Morning Bird noticed that there were some holes in the bottom of her shoe. He moved his toes inside of his own soft moccasins. He thought of the many skins hanging up to dry, with which his mother would make other moccasins for his brothers and sisters.

Morning Bird made up his mind to ask his mother to make a pair for this girl with the glowing hair. His mother might even have a pair already made which he could take along to the feast tomorrow.

The girl was rubbing her other foot now. The shoe she had just taken off was as thin and old as the first.

Her golden hair fell about her face as she leaned forward, holding her bare foot in both hands to warm it.

"Yes," said Morning Bird to himself, "she shall have a pair of moccasins with beads the color of her hair."

Suddenly a stick snapped under Morning Bird. The girl sat up and looked over toward the woods with frightened blue eyes. Then she slipped her feet quickly into her shoes and hurried off.

The bucket knocked against her legs as she ran, splashing water on her long, full skirt.

The shadows of the forest were growing longer as Morning Bird paddled his canoe toward his father's lodge. The darkness came early on these cold days, for the Sun God was far away, over the edge of the world.

When Morning Bird entered the lodge, his mother, Flying Cloud, filled a wooden bowl with hot food and handed it to him. Then she went back to her work.

Morning Bird watched her as he ate. Flying Cloud was sewing beads on a new pair of moccasins which were almost finished.

His eyes were shining as he watched his mother sewing on the blue and yellow beads. The yellow ones were like the hair of the girl at the spring, whom he called, in his thoughts, Bright Star. The blue beads were the color of her eyes.

Morning Bird went over to his mother. "I should like to have those moccasins," he said, picking up one of them.

Flying Cloud looked at him with surprise. "But these are too small for you, my son," she said. "I am making them for Little Roseblossom."

Hearing her mother, Roseblossom at once came running across from the other side of the lodge. Her dark eyes flashed at her brother. "You cannot have them!" she cried. "They are mine!"

Morning Bird saw that he would have to tell the whole story before there would be any chance of his getting the new moccasins.

"I do not want them for myself," he said. "I wish to give them to someone else. I would like to take them to the white men's feast tomorrow.

"This afternoon I saw a girl in the white men's village who was getting water at the spring," he went on.

"Her shoes had holes in the bottom, and she had to stop to shake out the little stones that crept in through the holes. The stones hurt her feet, and the cold air bit them. It was not good."

"She shall not have my moccasins," cried Little Roseblossom, grabbing the one in Morning Bird's hands. "The white men can make their own shoes."

Flying Cloud stopped sewing, and she stared into the fire. "It is good to give to others," she said at last. "Massasoit and his braves will take many deer to the feast of our white friends tomorrow.

"And you, Morning Bird, shall take a gift to the white girl who needs shoes. Little Roseblossom, you shall have another pair of moccasins, the same as these. We have other skins and other beads. Will you not agree to this, my little one?"

Little Roseblossom did not speak, and her face was not very happy. But slowly she handed the moccasin back to Morning Bird.

Flying Cloud nodded and took up her work once more. "Giving to others," she said softly, "is a way of thanking the Great Spirit, who gives all good things to his children.

"We make feasts to thank him, and we dance and sing of his wonders in the sky above and on the earth below. But giving is also thanks."

At sunrise the next day, Morning Bird put on his finest clothes. He fastened a bright feather over one ear, and he painted his face red and blue.

Then he tucked the new moccasins inside his shirt and took his place with the other Indians.

Five of the strongest men, each carrying a deer over his shoulders, came up and stood behind Chief Massasoit. Then the long line of Indians moved proudly toward the white men's settlement, bearing their gifts to the feast of Thanksgiving.

Showing Friendship

Suppose that Bright Star had started visiting the Indian camp after the Thanksgiving feast and that she and Roseblossom had become friends. This rhyme tells how the girls might have shown their friendship for each other. If you know what words rhyme with *wear*, you will have no trouble in reading the rhyme.

When Indian girls are friends, they wear
Rings woven from each other's h__.
Roseblossom said, "Would Bright Star d__
To cut a lock of her long h__,
So we could make a pretty p__
Of woven friendship rings to w__?"

Thought Bright Star, "All my friends would st__
At me if I should cut my h__.
But still, it doesn't seem quite f__
To tell her that I cannot sp__
One little lock from all my h__
To make some friendship rings to w__."

So Bright Star said, "I'll gladly sh__,
For friendship's sake, a lock of h__.
But when you cut it, please take c__
To choose a place to cut it wh__
It's very thick. I'd hardly d__
To go home with a spot that's b__."

And so they made a lovely p__
Of woven friendship rings to w__.
And Bright Star's friends *did* stop to st__,
But at her finger, not her h__.
For Bright Star proudly showed them, th__,
A ring of black and golden h__.

Part of What?

Write the word that should appear in each blank.

1. An Indian is part of a ___.
   (tribe, gap, paddle)
2. A finger is part of a ___.
   (moccasin, scale, hand)
3. A page is part of a ___.
   (book, coffee, Massasoit)
4. A skirt is part of a ___.
   (dress, petal, canoe)
5. A link is part of a ___.
   (pouch, chain, suffix)
6. Wheels are part of a ___.
   (lodge, carriage, armor)
7. A sail is part of a ___.
   (ship, settlement, bead)
8. Bars are part of a ___.
   (rein, encyclopedia, cage)
9. Legs are part of a ___.
   (temple, hull, bench)
10. A word is part of a ___.
    (screen, costume, dictionary)

Word Pictures

This story has beautiful word pictures, such as, "Lightly as the brush of a feather," and "The far-off glowing of a bright, bright star." These lines make you feel or see what the writer is telling about.

Write the number of the page on which you find a word picture of each of these things:

1. The ship which brought the settlers
2. Bright Star's hair
3. All the other children of the settlement

Johann Riehl was hiding behind the low stone wall as he peered out at the children going by.

There were two of them — a boy about Johann's age and a girl a little younger. Every morning Johann lay behind the stone wall and watched them breathlessly.

"Goblins!" he whispered to himself when they were safely gone. "Goblins!"

House of the

Singing

They weren't, of course, and Johann knew it. But the word *goblins* had a special meaning for Johann.

Across the sea in Germany, Johann's great-uncle had used it when Johann's parents had begged him to come with them to America.

"No, no," he had said with a shake of his head. "Once I have been there, and that is enough. I am too old to go fighting goblins now!"

The strange words had gone round and round in Johann's head. Finally he had said to his mother, "Mother, are there *really* goblins in this Iowa that we go to?"

Windows

His mother had laughed. "No, Johann. Your great-uncle means only the strange ways of the people we will meet, and the new English language. To him, these are as fearsome as goblins, and he has no longer the young, strong heart to beat them off."

Johann's heart was young and strong, but now it hid a deep, growing worry.

Oh, he didn't fear the new English language! Hadn't he spent a whole year learning it? But what about these strange Americans — other boys his age?

He remembered what his great-uncle had told him about the American children.

"Oh, such creatures!" he had said. "They do nothing but play baseball and eat pie and ice cream! And their talk, it is outlandish! 'Jumping catfish' they say, and 'Nuts.'"

It was March when they set out for America — Johann, his mother and his father, and the twenty-two canaries Mother could not leave behind. The trip was cold and unpleasant, across a gray and foggy sea.

But springtime arrived in America just when the Riehls did. And Johann thought each mile they crossed to Iowa was more beautiful than the last. Oh, this was a good land, a fine, rich, strong land. Johann loved it already!

They spent the first week in fixing up the old farmhouse that was to be their new home.

While he and his mother cleaned the new house, Father had covered the front windows, inside and out, with fine new screens. They were more than a foot deep — these windows — and with Father's new screens, they made wonderful cages for the twenty-two canaries.

But now the work of fixing up the new house was finished, and today Johann was to start to school.

His heart was not yet ready to face the dreadful American goblins, but the rest of him was ready. His hair was brushed flat under the little pancake hat. His short, tight coat and his short pants had just been pressed.

Johann said good-by to his mother and marched out of the door. But once he was outside, he circled quickly around to the barn. His heart beat fast.

To do battle with these American goblins, Johann needed just the right uniform. And, luckily, he had found the one he needed yesterday, quite by chance. Hanging in the barn, dusty and forgotten, was a huge pair of overalls.

Just such overalls, though smaller, had the American boy worn. And so different-looking were they from Johann's own clothes, that Johann had been sick at heart. But now . . .

Carefully Johann pinned the overalls to his size with many safety pins. Then he went out onto the road.

Ahead of him walked the two American goblins, the girl and boy he had watched as he hid behind the stone wall.

The boy looked back and, seeing Johann, he stopped and waited. He stared strangely at Johann during the whole minute that it took Johann to catch up with them. Then the boy spoke. "Hi!" he said.

The careful "how-do-you-do" that Johann had practiced in his English class choked in his throat. He swallowed hard. Then, in a low, steady voice, he answered, "Hi."

"Are you going to school?"

Johann nodded. They fell into step.

"My name's Peter Gates, and this is Jane. What's your name?"

"Jo — Joe Riehl." Johann waved back toward the stone farmhouse to show them where he lived.

Jane squealed with delight. "Oh, Peter. He lives in the house with the singing windows! I *told* you somebody nice must live there!"

Johann took a deep breath. "Jumping catfish!" he exclaimed. "Is that what you call it?"

When they arrived at the schoolhouse, Peter led Johann up to the teacher's desk and said, "Here's a new boy, Miss Swift. His name's Joe Riehl."

Miss Swift smiled. "Hello, Joe," she said. "We're glad to have you." She led him to a seat in the back of the room.

Here, all about him, were American children. They were *real* Americans, and they all seemed to think that Johann was American, too. But what if they should find out that he wasn't?

Miss Swift came over to him after a while. "Now, Joe," she said with a friendly smile, "have you a report card from your last school?"

Johann reached under the huge overalls, into his pants pocket. His fingers closed over his report card, and he started to pull it out.

Then his hand stopped. He *couldn't* show the report card from the school in Germany, he just *couldn't!*

"Did you forget it?" Miss Swift asked in an understanding way. "Never mind. Tomorrow will be all right. I'll put you with Peter today."

Then a bell rang. Peter came up to Johann. "What do you want to play?"

Johann answered at once. "Baseball," he said, remembering what his great-uncle had said.

The next thing he knew, Peter was putting a long sort of club into his hand. Then he was pushed into place facing a boy with a ball.

Suddenly the ball was coming right at him! Johann gave a surprised yell and held up the club to keep from being hit.

The ball cracked against the club and shot back over the head of the boy who had thrown it. Eager hands pushed Johann. "Run, Joe, RUN!"

What had he done? What must he run from? He tried to run, but something was all tangled up around his feet. It was his overalls, slipping down from his shoulders.

But still he *did* run. And still, eager hands pushed at him and pulled at him, turning him in a big circle. Suddenly, he stumbled and fell forward, right where he'd started.

"Home run! Home run!" the boys shouted.

Johann tried to get up, but the pins in his overalls had come undone.

Peter came hurrying to help him. "Don't worry about it," he said. "You were great!"

Johann returned to his seat. He was glowing with happiness. But then Miss Swift started to talk about a party, an all-American party, and Johann's spirits sank again. He and his parents would never pass for all-Americans, never!

When school was out, Miss Swift came over to Johann and Peter and Jane. "I think I'll walk home with you," she told Johann. "It will be a good time to get your report card."

Johann couldn't say a word. Now they would find out that he wasn't an all-American.

Suddenly he thought of a plan. "I'll go ahead," he said quickly. "I — I'll tell Mother you're coming."

He raced toward his house. "Oh, Mother!" he cried, opening the door. "They are coming!"

His mother hurried out of the kitchen, drying her hands on her big apron. "What is it, boy? Who comes?"

"The teacher, Mother! Oh, you must hurry, please hurry. Make yourself fine in the good dress. And talk only American. Oh, Mother, you do understand, don't you? They are coming!"

"Yes, yes!" she cried. "I understand." She ran upstairs, too excited to notice Johann's strange costume.

Then Johann hurried back to meet the others. He was saved! Mother would put on the dress that Great-uncle had bought when he was here. It was just a kitchen work dress, but at least it was *American!*

Slowly, slowly, Johann led the company through the gate.

"Look, Miss Swift!" Jane cried. "See the windows! Look at all the beautiful canaries!"

"Oh, beautiful!" exclaimed Miss Swift, and then she said again, softly, "Beautiful." But this time her voice sounded different, and she wasn't looking at the windows any more. Johann looked quickly toward the front door.

His mother was standing there. Her face was pink from hurry, but her eyes were glowing with gentleness and love.

She had done what her son had asked. She had put on her finest — the full, flowered skirt and tiny coat of her Sunday-best back in Germany.

Proudly, now, she held out both her hands toward them and said, in her most careful English, "Welcome."

Johann's throat was choking with a great love for her. Oh, it didn't matter at all that she had spoiled his secret. She had tried so hard to please him. He marched up to her side and faced the Americans fiercely.

"Miss Swift, this is my mother," he began. And just so there would be no mistake, he added, "And my name is not Joe, either. It's Johann. We are not Americans, like you. We come from across the sea."

Miss Swift smiled. "Don't we all, Joe? Isn't that what America is — a gathering place for those who have the courage to cross the sea and find it? That's just what has made our country big and strong, Joe.

"It takes strong people to leave behind them all that is dear and start out to meet a different world."

Johann stared at his new teacher as she went on. "It takes people like you and your parents to show that kind of courage. And it takes people like Peter's grandfather, and my own parents, who also left their homes to cross the sea.

"You'll see what I mean, Joe, at the all-American party. We'll all be wearing our Old World clothes, and your mother must be sure to come in that lovely costume."

Johann's heart was fairly bursting with happiness. So this was what all-American meant! He turned to his new American friends. "Come on in!" he said warmly. "The windows and the canaries look even prettier from the inside!"

Proudly Johann led them into his home. And sunshine poured into his heart through a thousand singing windows.

Johann's Worries

Johann was greatly worried about the goblins he would meet in the United States. Each problem he had to face during the first day at school seemed like an awful goblin to him. On your paper write what Johann did when each of these problems arose:

1. His German clothes did not look like the clothes which American boys and girls wore to school.
2. Miss Swift asked for his report card.
3. He had to play an American game at recess.
4. Miss Swift walked home with Johann to pick up his report card.

The All-American Boy

Write the answers to these questions:

1. What fact about himself was Johann trying to hide?
2. Why was he trying to hide this fact?
3. When his teacher and his friends discovered this fact, did they think any less of Johann? Why?

Different-Looking Pairs That Rhyme

You can hear that the words *band* and *land* rhyme with each other. You can see that both of those words end with the same three letters, *and*. However, not all pairs of rhyming words end with the same letters. *Flight* and *kite* rhyme, but their last few letters are not the same. Other pairs of rhyming words that end in different letters are *here* and *deer*, *care* and *pair*, *scale* and *mail*.

From the following lists of words, find the pairs that rhyme with each other. Write those ten pairs.

sigh	call	worst	yes
study	canoe	boast	prairie
bawl	clean	canary	thirst
screen	hi	express	report
drew	bloody	court	most

Match the Sounds

Think of the vowel sound in the name of each picture. You will hear that same vowel sound in the accented syllables of two of the words beside each picture. Write those words on your paper.

1.
   huge
   stuff
   duty
   bucket

2.
   unto
   goblin
   glow
   woven

3.
   jeans
   paddle
   report
   screen

4.
   cause
   mount
   lord
   allowance

5.
   rifle
   quiz
   vinegar
   hi

6.
   scale
   card
   scar
   cable

7.
   boast
   Tony
   probably
   broad

8.
   Canada
   Italy
   errand
   tangled

LOOKING BACK AND REMEMBERING
Who Did What?

Write the name of the story that tells about each of these people:

1. a. An Indian who gave a present to a girl
   b. An Indian who helped a sister and brother
2. a. A boy who won a prize
   b. A boy who made a home run
3. a. A sister who helped her brother get the mail through
   b. A sister who gave her moccasins to her brother
4. a. A boy who was afraid of goblins
   b. Two girls who were afraid of Indians

What's My Name?

Which of the following people might have said each of the sentences listed below? Write the names on your paper after the numbers.

Sally Porter   Mr. Ellett   Ma
Pa   Mrs. Riehl   Homan Walsh
Johann Riehl   Massasoit   Laura

1. "I am Morning Bird's father."
2. "I came from Germany with my parents."
3. "I have a sister named Carrie."
4. "I told my daughters not to let my dog loose."
5. "I rode for the Pony Express."
6. "I gave five dollars to the boy who flew his kite across the Niagara River."
7. "I baked cornbread for two Indians."
8. "I linked two countries with my kite."
9. "I put on my best dress to please my son."

Words and What They Do

Each numbered word may be used to tell about one of the things beside it. Write each number on your paper. Beside it put the word you choose.

1. fierce   cable, Indian
2. tasty   professor, licorice
3. yellow   canary, nickel
4. compound   word, screen
5. merciful   person, greed
6. sharp   union, sword
7. weak   baby, costume
8. long   Germany, report
9. beaded   moccasins, errand
10. huge   giant, dwarf

Rules You Remember

On your paper write the word that belongs in each blank.

1. In a one-syllable word that ends in silent *e*, the vowel sound is usually __. (long, short)
2. In a one-syllable word which ends in one consonant with only one vowel before it, the vowel sound is usually __. (long, short)
3. When two vowels come together in a syllable, they usually stand for the __ (long, short) sound of the __ (first, second) vowel.
4. The number of syllables in a word is usually the same as the number of __ (vowel, consonant) sounds.
5. When two __ stand between two __ (vowels, consonants), the syllables are usually divided between the two __. (vowels, consonants)

WORDBOOK

a·cre \\'āk-r\\ 43,560 square feet of land. There are six houses on this acre.

aim \\'ām\\ 1. To point an object at something that one wishes to hit. 2. The end for which one works.

al·low·ance \\ə-'laů-əns\\ Money given to someone every week or month.

am·bi·tious \\am-'bish-əs\\ Eager to learn or to get ahead.

A·mos \\'ā-məs\\ A man's name.

An·ya \\'an-yə\\ A girl's name.

ap·peal \\ə-'pēl\\ 1. To ask or beg for something. 2. A call for help.

bead \\'bēd\\ A little ball with a hole through it for stringing with other beads.

boast \\'bōst\\ To tell how smart you are or how wonderful your family or pet is.

Bo·az \\'bō-az\\ A man's name.

bore \\'bōr\\ Did bear; carried.

buck·et \\'bək-ət\\ A pail. The boy got a bucket of water from the well.

burst \\'bərst\\ 1. To fly apart suddenly. 2. To speak or move suddenly.

ca·ble \\'kāb-l\\ A thick, strong rope, often made of wire.

Can·a·da \\'kan-əd-ə\\ The country north of ours.

car·riage \\'kar-ij\\ Something on wheels for carrying people; as, a baby carriage.

Car·rie \\'kar-ē\\ A girl's name.

Car·ver, Mo·ses \\'kärv-r, 'mō-ziz\\ The man who took George Washington Carver into his home.

cham·pi·on·ship \\'champ-ē-ən-ship\\ First place in a game or other contest.

cheat \\'chēt\\ To trick; to win unfairly.

choke \\'chōk\\ 1. To stop up; to shut off. 2. To stick. The words choked in her throat.

Clan·cy \\'klan-sē\\ A last name.

coax \\'kōks\\ To beg over and over again, in a pleasant way.

col·lege \\'käl-ij\\ A school that is above high school.

cos·tume \\'käs-tüm\\ A dress or suit, often an unusual one, like a Halloween costume.

cra·zy \\'krā-zē\\ 1. Unsound in mind. 2. Queer; wild. He can certainly think of crazy things to do.

crit·i·cism \\'krit-ə-siz-m\\ The act of finding fault.

crit·i·cize \\'krit-ə-sīz\\ To tell someone what he has said or done that you don't like; to find fault.

Cun·ning·ham, Glenn \\'kən-ing-ham, 'glen\\ The boy who became a champion runner, even though his legs had been badly burned.

cush·ion \\'küsh-n\\ A soft pillow, often used in a chair.

dis·ease \\di-'zēz\\ A sickness.

dumb \\'dəm\\ 1. Not smart; stupid. 2. Not able to speak.

du·ty \\'düt-ē\\ The right thing to do. It is my duty to do my homework before I play.

dwarf \\'dwȯrf\\ One who is much smaller than most people. In stories a dwarf is often a kind of fairy.

Elk·hart \\'elk-härt\\ A town in southwestern Kansas.

El·lett \\'el-ət\\ A last name.

Key to Sounds

		ī	mile, lying	ch	chair
		i	mill, indeed, here	l	little
		ō	go, arrow	n	seven
ā	ate, they	ȯ	horn, dog, fall, paw	ng	ring
a	hat, land	ȯi	oil, toy	r	letter
ä	far, father, got	ü	blue, too, used \\'yüzd\\	sh	wish
aů	out, how	ů	put, good, poor	th	thank
ē	meet, begin, easy	ə	ago, up, perhaps	th	than
e	met, care		her, hurt, bird	zh	garage

The Key to Sounds above is used by permission. For further information see *Webster's Elementary Dictionary*, © 1959 by G. & C. Merriam Co., Publishers of the Merriam-Webster Dictionaries.

en·cour·age \in-'kər-ij\ To help; to cheer. The doctor's visit encouraged my sick brother.

er·rand \'er-ənd\ A short trip to do some special thing.

fade \'fād\ To lose color. That green chair will fade in the sunlight.

fake \'fāk\ Something that is false or tricky.

fe·ver \'fēv-r\ A sickness in which the body becomes warmer than usual.

Fran·cis \'fran-sis\ A man's name.

frown \'fraùn\ To look displeased by drawing the eyebrows together.

gap \'gap\ 1. An opening between two places or things. 2. A mountain pass.

Get·tys·burg \'get-iz-bərg\ A town in southern Pennsylvania.

gob·lin \'gäb-lən\ A bad kind of fairy.

Gub·bio \'güb-yō\ A town near the center of Italy.

har·mon·i·ca \här-'män-ik-ə\ A small instrument, held in the hand and played by the mouth.

hos·pi·tal \'häs-pit-l\ A place where sick people or animals are cared for.

in·vite \in-'vīt\ To ask someone to make one a visit.

I·o·wa \'ī-ə-wə\ A state a little north of the middle of our country.

kite \'kīt\ A light framework covered with cloth or paper. It is made to fly in the air at the end of a long string.

knight \'nīt\ In the Middle Ages, a brave man who had promised to do good and to fight for his king or lord.

Lau·ra \'lòr-ə\ A girl's name.

lic·o·rice \'lik-r-ish\ A kind of candy that is flavored with the dried root of the licorice plant.

limp \'limp\ To walk unevenly. The dog limped after he was hurt.

link \'lingk\ That which joins two or more things.

lodge \'läj\ An Indian cabin or house.

lord \'lòrd\ In the Middle Ages, one who was the leader of many knights.

lynx \'lingks\ A wildcat with long legs and a short tail.

Mas·sa·soit \mas-ə-'sòit\ The chief of a friendly Indian tribe at the time of the first Thanksgiving in America.

Mc·Cor·mick, Cy·rus \mə-'kòr-mik, 'sī-rəs\ The man who built a reaper for cutting wheat.

Meade, George \'mēd, 'jòrj\ The Northern leader at Gettysburg.

mer·cy \'mər-sē\ Kindness; forgiveness.

Mi·das \'mī-dəs\ The king who wanted all the gold in the world.

mir·a·cle \'mir-ək-l\ A happening that is so wonderful it is hard to believe.

moc·ca·sin \'mäk-əs-n\ A soft leather shoe without a heel.

Mount Mo·ri·ah \'maùnt mə-'rī-ə\ A hill in a country far across the sea.

mus·sel \'məs-l\ A shellfish that lives either in the ocean or in fresh water.

Ne·o·sho \nē-'ō-shō\ A town in southwestern Missouri.

Ni·ag·a·ra \nī-'ag-rə\ A river and also a great waterfall between our country and Canada.

ped·al \'ped-l\ The part of a bicycle on which the foot is placed.

peer \'pir\ To look searchingly.

pet·al \'pet-l\ One of the white or colored parts of a flower.

post·al \'pōst-l\ A card for mailing, with a stamp printed on it.

prin·ci·pal \'prins-əp-l\ The head of a school.

prob·lem \'präb-ləm\ A hard question. Mary tried to work out the answer to her problem.

pro·fes·sor \prə-'fes-r\ A teacher, usually in a college.

push·mo·bile \\'pùsh-mō-bēl\\ A small racing wagon that must be pushed.

quiz \\'kwiz\\ A test in which questions are asked.

raid \\'rād\\ An attack by armed men.

rap \\'rap\\ To knock or tap.

reap \\'rēp\\ To cut grain.

re·treat \\rē-'trēt\\ To draw back from a dangerous place.

Rick·en·back·er, Ed·die \\'rik-n-bak-r, 'ed-ē\\ A well-known flier.

Riehl, Jo·hann \\'rēl, 'yō-hän\\ A German boy's name.

ri·fle \\'rīf-l\\ A gun fired from the shoulder.

Ro·land \\'rō-lənd\\ A man's name.

sac·ri·fice \\'sak-rə-fīs\\ Giving up one thing for a better thing.

salt·y \\'sȯl-tē\\ Tasting of salt; having salt in it.

scarred \\'skärd\\ Marked by a burn or cut that has healed over.

schwa \\'shwä\\ 1. The sound of *u* in *up* and *upon* and of *e* in *her* and *perhaps*. 2. The sign (ə) for this sound.

score \\'skōr\\ The number of points one makes in a game or other contest.

scrap \\'skrap\\ A small, leftover piece of food, paper, cloth, and so forth.

scythe \\'sīth\\ A tool with a bow-shaped knife that is fastened to a long wooden handle.

sheaves \\'shēvz\\ Bundles of grain.

shield \\'shēld\\ A flat piece of armor carried in the hand.

sor·row·ful \\'sär-əf-l\\ Very sad.

stat·ue \\'stach-ü\\ The likeness of a living being, often made from stone.

steal \\'stēl\\ To take what belongs to another.

stoop \\'stüp\\ To lean down.

stray \\'strā\\ 1. To wander away. 2. Lost and wandering.

strug·gle \\'strəg-l\\ 1. A fight; very hard work. 2. To fight or work hard.

stu·dent \\'stüd-nt\\ One who goes to school, or one who studies.

swal·low \\'swäl-ō\\ To make food or water go down one's throat.

Syl·ves·ter \\sil-'vest-r\\ A last name.

tan·gled \\'tang-gld\\ Mixed up. This string is all tangled up.

team \\'tēm\\ All the players on one side in a game.

tem·ple \\'temp-l\\ A building set apart as a reminder of God or gods.

thus \\'thəs\\ In this way.

tore \\'tōr\\ Did tear. 1. Pulled apart. 2. Moved along very fast.

tri·al \\'trī-əl\\ 1. A test. 2. Used for testing. 3. The hearing of a case.

tuck \\'tək\\ To put something where it will be held tightly. He tucked his cap under his arm.

Tus·ke·gee In·sti·tute \\təs-'kē-gē 'ins-tə-tüt\\ A school of higher learning in Alabama.

ug·ly \\'əg-lē\\ Very unpleasant.

un·ion \\'yün-yən\\ The act of joining together for some good reason.

un·less \\ən-'les\\ If not.

un·to \\'ən-tü; 'ən-tə\\ To. "I will lift up mine eyes unto the hills."

val·en·tine \\'val-ən-tīn\\ A card which is given on Valentine's Day.

Walsh, Ho·man \\'wȯlsh, 'hō-mən\\ A boy who loved kites.

waste \\'wāst\\ To spend or use carelessly.

whiz \\'hwiz\\ To go very fast, usually with a humming sound.

wo·ven \\'wōv-n\\ Made as cloth is made.

Yan·kee \\'yangk-ē\\ A name given to anyone who was born in the northeastern part of our country.

STORIES TO READ AND REMEMBER

Blaze and the Forest Fire. C. W. Anderson. This is an exciting story about the courage of a boy and his horse.

The Hundred Dresses. Eleanor Estes. Wanda had only one dress, but she could draw beautiful dresses. Even those who made fun of her patched dress learned to admire her.

The Homemade Year. Mildred Lawrence. A girl who has lived in the city all her life has many adventures as she learns to love the country and her country cousins.

A Street of Little Shops. Margery Williams Bianco. Here are seven gay stories about the adventures of some people who lived on one little street.

Down, Down the Mountain. Ellis Credle. Two mountain children who want beautiful, shining, creaky-squeaky shoes, work hard until they get them.

Told Under the Stars and Stripes. American Association of Childhood Education. In these stories, new Americans from all over the world learn to love their new country.

Young Readers Sports Stories. Abraham L. Furman. These are thrilling stories of baseball, basketball, swimming, and other sports.

Lou Gehrig, Boy of the Sand Lots. Guernsey Van Riper, Jr. Lou Gehrig was a great baseball player who lived by his motto, "Keep your eye on the ball. Meet it squarely."

That Lively Man, Ben Franklin. Jeanette Eaton. This is the story of a great American who worked joyously all his life to defend the rights of men everywhere.

The Wright Brothers, Pioneers of American Aviation. Quentin Reynolds. People laughed at the idea of man's being able to fly. But the Wrights kept trying until they succeeded.

Builders for Progress. Mathilda Schirmer, Editor. These men and women worked all their lives to make our lives better.

A Treasury of Hero Stories. Joanna Strong and Tom Leonard. Some men are heroes because they fight for their country. Others fight disease and unfairness. But all are brave men.

The Shoemaker's Apron. Parker Fillmore. In the story, "The Twelve Months," kindness finally overcomes greed.

A Wonderbook and Tanglewood Tales. Nathaniel Hawthorne. This book is full of interesting myths and legends.

The Willow Whistle. Cornelia Meigs. This is an exciting story of a boy and a girl long ago and their Indian friend.

Chi-Wee. Grace Moon. You will enjoy reading about the adventures of this gay little Indian girl.

Little House in the Big Woods. Laura Ingalls Wilder. The children in this story lived in the wilderness long ago.

VOCABULARY INFORMATION

Number of New Words: 377

A word is counted as new if it, or a common variant form of it, does not appear on the American Book Company Core Vocabulary for Use in Grade 4. This Core Vocabulary is composed of words common to at least five out of eight series of basic readers through Grade 3. Therefore, it can be safely assumed that the words in the Core Vocabulary for use in Grade 4 are within the reading vocabulary of pupils of fourth-grade reading ability.

Poems and bibliographical entries are excluded from the vocabulary control.

The stories, the activities, the directions for activities, and the wordbook of *Paths to Follow* have been written to the following readability specifications.

Maximum number of new words per sentence	1
Minimum number of familiar words between new words	20
Maximum number of new words per 200 words	4
Maximum number of words per sentence	24
Maximum number of lines per paragraph	9
Maximum number of new words per story	17
Maximum number of new words per wordbook entry	1

143. control
144. ....
145. ....
146. dictionary
147. ....

UNIT 4

150. sacrifice
     Walter
     Reed
     Yankee
151. raids
     rifle
     probably
     main
152. steep
     craziest
     diseases
153. stealing
     supplies
154. ....
155. ....
156. speech
     fever
     Washing-
     ton
157. ....
158. ....
159. Moses
     Carver
     Negro
160. petals
     Neosho
161. God
     ambitious
     Sue
     blossoms
162. shirt
163. professor
     Iowa
164. students
     Tuskegee
     Institute
165. ....

166. ....
167. ....
168. Addams
     Hull
169. English
     appeal
     language
170. Tony
     neighbor-
     hood
     clubs
171. hunger
172. trust
     honestly
173. impossible
     pressed
174. ....
175. quiz
     encyclo-
     pedia
     Ellen
     Gates
     Starr
176. Francis
     Gubbio
     comfort
177. faithfully
     reap
     shield
178. beast
     battle
179. doubt
180. unto
     treated
181. ....
182. Italy
183. harvest
     Cyrus Mc-
     Cormick
     success
184. machine
     invention
185. scythe
     invent
     grain
     Ruff's

186. acres
     prince
187. ....
188. fake
     Taylor
189. ....
190. ....
191. ....
192. ....
193. ....

UNIT 5

196. Midas
197. perfectly
198. ....
199. precious
     statue
200. ....
201. ....
202. suffixes
203. ....
204. mercy
205. thus
206. ....
207. knights
     armor
     deed
208. lord
     Roland
     com-
     manded
209. ....
210. ....
211. sword
     size
212. report
213. ....
214. ....
215. compound
216. Mount
     Moriah
     sheaves
217. share
     Amos
     Boaz

218. bore
     slept
219. temple
220. spirit
221. greedy
     ham
222. dwarfs
223. grind
224. ....
225. ....
226. ....
227. sink
     sank
228. ....
229. bawl
230. ....
231. ....

UNIT 6

234. Homan
     Walsh
     Niagara
     Canada
235. gap
     Ellett
     link
     union
236. cable
     tangled
237. ....
238. fiercely
239. huge
240. ....
241. ....
244. express
245. buckets
     pouches
     dragged
246. ....
247. dead
     coffee
248. stuffing

249. blood
250. stooped
251. ....
252. duty
253. ....
254. chained
     Laura
     prairie
255. weak
256. Carrie
     skirt
257. ....
258. ....
259. ....
260. ....
261. ....
262. paddled
     tribe
     Massasoit
     canoe
     settlement
263. screen
264. glowing
     costumes
     moccasins
265. beads
     lodge
266. ....
267. ....
268. woven
269. ....
270. Johann
     Riehl
     goblins
     Germany
271. canaries
272. ....
273. ....
274. ....
275. ....
276. ....
277. ....
278. ....
279. ....
280. ....
281. ....

A Beka Book Publications, an outgrowth of Pensacola Christian School, is a Christian ministry designed to meet the need for Christian textbooks and teaching aids for Christian schools. The purpose of this publications ministry is to help Christian schools reach children and young people for the Lord and train them in the Christian way of life.

If we can be of further help to your ministry, please write **A Beka Book Publications,** Box 18000, Pensacola, Florida 32523.